The Teacher's Guidebook
to
Piano Literature

A Recommended Listing of Graded Repertoire for Elementary, Intermediate and Lower Advanced Students

By
Alice M. Kern

and

Helen M. Titus

University of Michigan
Ann Arbor, Michigan

J. W. EDWARDS, Publisher, Inc.
Ann Arbor, Michigan

First Edition, Second Printing: April 1955
First Edition, Third Printing: September 1955

Library of Congress Catalog Card Number: 55-7793

J. W. EDWARDS, Publisher, Inc.
Ann Arbor, Michigan

FOREWORD

This book is primarily designed for the convenience of teachers of piano. It lists nearly four thousand available compositions which have been selected particularly for the elementary and intermediate student.

The graded listing of materials presented is the result of many years of study and examination of music from the teacher's point of view. It grew out of a course in "Methods and Materials for Piano Teachers" which we have taught for some time at the University of Michigan. We received further encouragement in our project from discussions and correspondence with colleagues throughout the country, from conferences and workshops with various organizations of piano teachers, and from many young inexperienced teachers who have sought our advice from time to time. These teachers have all requested a concrete listing of materials which would best suit their needs. We have tried to meet these needs by listing each composition according to grade level and according to an arbitrary chronological classification, so that it will facilitate the planning of a well balanced repertoire. We have mentioned various collections in which each composition may be found, giving names of publishers and indicating which compositions are also published separately.

Our procedure has been the careful examination of each work listed, with reference to its general grade level and its merit in the field of piano literature. Each work has been studied, analyzed, and evaluated for its suitability in a recommended list. Although we realize the excellent teaching value of many other publications, we have limited the list to composers whose general output has seemed significant. Methods for beginners have not been included, nor have the standard exercises.

We have used the more flexible divisions of grade levels indicated by Lower Elementary, Upper Elementary, Intermediate, and Lower Advanced. Because of the uneven musical and technical development of many students, the standards of accomplishment at the end of a given period will be different with each student. It is suggested that the teacher also be flexible in the use of materials from the graded lists.

Our arbitrary breakdown of the classification of the music by centuries may arouse controversy. Because of the varied styles of composers of a specific period, it is sometimes difficult to decide where to place these composers, historically speaking. For that reason, we have included after each composer's name his birth and death dates, as a matter of convenience. We have arbitrarily included the works of composers who died before 1825 under the listings of the sixteenth, seventeenth and eighteenth centuries; later composers who died before 1910 under the nineteenth century and composers who are still living or who died after 1910 under the twentieth century.

We hope that the further study of the music recommended in this book will provide as much stimulation and be of as much practical value as it has been to us.

Since much music of importance is being continuously published, it is our plan to issue supplements to this basic list at regular intervals.

Alice M. Kern

Helen M. Titus

Ann Arbor, Michigan
April, 1954

We wish to acknowledge the generous assistance of Mrs. Orien Dalley of the University Music House, Ann Arbor, Michigan, in procuring materials for our study.

We are also grateful for the advice and support of Professor Joseph Brinkman and other faculty members of the School of Music, University of Michigan.

Mr. Lee Pattison and other associates throughout the country have been extremely helpful in contributing many valuable suggestions.

CONTENTS

SECTION I

LOWER ELEMENTARY

GRADES I AND II

MUSIC OF THE SIXTEENTH, SEVENTEENTH
AND EIGHTEENTH CENTURIES

Composer	Title	Publisher	Volume or Collection
AGINCOURT, F. de (1684-1757)	Le Colin Maillard	BH	Airs and Dances, Bk. I
BACH, C.P.E. (1714-1788)	Allegretto in F	C	Eighteenth Century Music, Vol. I (No. 4)
	Allegro di molto	K	The Direct Path (Hermann)
	March in C	O	Piano Music for Young Wolfgang
	Minuet in F	C	Eighteenth Century Music, Vol. I
	Minuet in F Minor	C	Eighteenth Century Music, Vol. I
BACH, J. C. F. (1732-1795)	Allegro in C	Sch	Clavierstücke für Anfänger
	Schwaebisch in D	Sch	Clavierstücke für Anfänger
	Minuet I in D	C	Eighteenth Century Music, Vol. I
		Sch	Menuetten fürs Clavier, (Kreutz)
	Minuet II in D	C	Eighteenth Century Music, Vol. I
		Sch	Menuetten fürs Clavier, (Kreutz)
BACH, J. S. (1685-1750)	Aria di Giovannini	K	Little Notebook for Anna Magdalena Bach
		BMC	Bach for Early Grades, Bk. I
	Aria, "So oft ich meine Tobackspfeife" (When My Pipe I Smoke)	K	Little Notebook for Anna Magdalena Bach
		BMC	Bach for Early Grades, Bk. I
	Aria in F	K	Little Notebook for Anna Magdalena Bach
		BMC	Bach for Early Grades, Bk. I
	Aria, "Warum betrübst du dich"	K	Little Notebook for Anna Magdalena Bach (pg. 102)
		GS	Master Series for the Young (pg. 4)
	Chorale, "Wie wohl ist mir"	K	Little Notebook for Anna Magdalena Bach
		BMC	Bach for Early Grades, Bk. I
	Chorale in E Minor	BMC	Bach for Early Grades, Bk. I
	Chorale, "Schaff's mit mir, Gott" (Do as Thou willst with me, O Lord)	BMC	Bach for Early Grades, Bk. I
	Hymn in F Major (I Rest in Thy Love)	GS	Master Series for the Young
		He	A Little Treasury of Classics, Bk. I (Lambert)
	Menuet in D Minor	K	Little Notebook for Anna Magdalena Bach
		K	The First Bach Book
		GS	First Lessons in Bach, Bk. I (Carroll)
		CF	Bach First Lessons, Bk. I (Carroll)
		BMC	Bach for Early Grades, Bk. I
		I	The Little Music Book of Anna Magdalena Bach

Composer	Title	Publisher	Volume or Collection
BACH, J. S. (cont.)		P	Notenbuch der Anna Magdalena Bach
	Menuet in G Minor	K	Little Notebook for Anna Magdalena Bach
		K	The First Bach Book
		GS	First Lessons in Bach, Bk. I (Carroll)
		CF	Bach First Lessons, Bk. I
		BMC	Bach for Early Grades, Bk. I
		GS	Master Series for the Young
		I	The Little Music Book of Anna Magdalena Bach
		P	Notenbuch der Anna Magdalena Bach
		PP	Hundred Best Short Classics, Bk. I
	Two Menuets in G	K	Little Notebook for Anna Magdalena Bach
		K	The First Bach Book
		GS	First Lessons in Bach, Bk. I (Carroll)
		CF	Bach, First Lessons, Bk. I (Carroll)
		BMC	Bach for Early Grades, Bk. I
		GS	Master Series for the Young
		I	The Little Music Book of Anna Magdalena Bach
		P	Notenbuch der Anna Magdalena Bach
		PP	Hundred Best Short Classics, Bk. I
	Minuet in G	GS	First Lessons in Bach, Bk. I, (Carroll) (No. 7)
		CF	Bach, First Lessons, Bk. I (Carroll) (No. 1)
	Minuets in G Minor	GS	First Lessons in Bach, Bk. I (Carroll) (Nos. 6 & 8)
		CF	Bach First Lessons, Bk. I (Nos. 6 & 8)
	Musette in D	K	Little Notebook for Anna Magdalena Bach
		K	The First Bach Book
		CS	First Lessons in Bach, Bk. I (Carroll)
		CF	Bach First Lessons, Bk. I (Carroll)
		BMC	Bach for Early Grades, Bk. I
		GS	Master Series for the Young
		I	The Little Music Book
		P	Notenbuch der Anna Magdalena Bach
		CF	Road to Piano Artistry, Vol. II (Scionti)
	Musette in G Major (from English Suite III)	K	English Suites
		PP	Hundred Best Short Classics, Bk. II
		K	The First Bach Book
		CF	Bach First Lessons, Bk. I (Carroll)
		GS	First Lessons in Bach, Bk. I (Carroll)
	Polonaise in G Minor	K	Little Notebook for Anna Magdalena Bach
		K	The First Bach Book
		BMC	Bach for Early Grades, Bk. I
		GS	Master Series for the Young (pg. 9)
		P	Notenbuch der Anna Magdalena Bach (pg. 10)
BACH, W. F. (1710-1784)	Minuet in E-flat	C	Eighteenth Century Music, Vol. I

Composer	Title	Publisher	Volume or Collection
BLOW, J. (1649-1708)	Song Tune	H	Contemporaries of Purcell
CLARK, J. (1670-1707)	Minuet in G	H	Contemporaries of Purcell
CORELLI, A. (1653-1713)	Sarabande in D Minor	P	Sonatinen Vorstufe (Preparatory Sonatina Album)
COUPERIN, F. (1668-1733)	Air in C	U	Old Masters for Young Pianists (Kuranda)
	Carnival	He	A Little Treasury of Classics, Bk. I (Lambert)
	Merry Fair Music	U	Old Masters for Young Pianists (Kuranda)
	The Tambourines	He	A Little Treasury of Classics, Bk. I (Lambert)
DANDRIEU, de (1684-1740)	Dance at the Fair	He	A Little Treasury of Classics, Bk. I (Lambert)
DAQUIN, C. (1694-1772)	Noël	BH	Airs and Dances, Bk. I (Dorolle)
DIEUPART, C. (-----1740)	Menuett in A	P	Contemporaries of Telemann
DUNCOMBE, W. (?)	Sonatina in C Vivace Trumpet Menuet Hunting Jig	BH	Early English Sonatinas (Rowley)
	Vivace (Sonatina in C)	He	Little Treasury of Sonatinas, Bk. I
FIOCCO, J. H. (1690- ?)	La Légère	BH	Airs and Dances, Bk. I (Dorolle)
FISCHER, J. K. F. (1650-1746)	From "The Notebook" Gavotte in G Menuet in D Menuet in D Minor Menuet in F Menuet in G Menuet in G Menuet in G	Sch	Notebook of Johann Kasper Ferd. Fischer (No. 8) (No. 3) (No. 12) (No. 1) (No. 2) (No. 6)
	Präludium in C	K	The Direct Path (Hermann)
GRAUPNER, C. (1683-1760)	Menuett in C Menuett in G	P	Contemporaries of Telemann
HANDEL, G. F. (1685-1759)	Menuett in G	He	A Little Treasury of Classics, Bk. I (Lambert)

Composer	Title	Publisher	Volume or Collection
HANDEL, G. F. (cont.)	Little Dances	Sch	Twenty Little Dances (Frey)
	Gavotte in D		(No. 11)
	Gavotte in G Minor		(No. 3)
	Menuett in A Minor		(No. 10)
	Menuett in B-flat		(No. 1)
	Menuett in F		(No. 6)
	Menuett in F		(No. 17)
	Menuett in G		(No. 4)
	Menuett in G Minor		(No. 13)
	Passepied in A		(No. 5)
	Passepied in C		(No. 9)
	Sarabande in F		(No. 2)
	Sarabande in F		(No. 8)
	Zwei Menuetto in G Minor		
HAYDN, J. (1732-1809)	Allegretto in B-flat	U	Little Dances for Young Folk (No. 5)
	Allegretto in F	U	Little Dances for Young Folk (No. 8)
		CF	Road to Piano Artistry, Vol. I (Scionti)
	Allegro Giocoso in C	U	Little Dances for Young Folk (No. 7)
	Allegro Maestoso	U	Little Dances for Young Folk (No. 12)
	Allegro Risoluto	U	Little Dances for Young Folk (No. 6)
	Allegro Vivace	U	Little Dances for Young Folk (No. 10)
	Country Dance in D	He	A Little Treasury of Classics, Bk. II (Lambert)
	Etude in G	CF	Road to Piano Artistry, Vol. I (Scionti)
	German Dance	He	A Little Treasury of Classics, Bk. II (Lambert)
	Moderato in A	U	Little Dances for Young Folk (No. 11)
	Moderato in G	U	Little Dances for Young Folk (No. 4)
HILLER, J. A. (1728-1804)	Minuetto in A	Sch	Simple Short Piano Pieces (Kreutz) (No. 2a)
	Minuetto in F	Sch	Simple Short Piano Pieces (Kreutz) (No. 5)
HOOK, J. (1746-1827)	Hunting Song	BH	Old English Worthies (Rowley)
KIRNBERGER, J. P. (1721-1783)	Minuetto in C	Sch	Clavierstücke für Anfänger
	Minuetto in G		
KUHNAU, J. (1660-1722)	Sarabande in F	GS	Introduction to Piano Classics, Vol. II (Mirovitch)
LÖHLEIN, G. S. (1727-1782)	Balletto	Sch	Clavierstücke für Anfänger
MOURET, J. J. (1682-1735)	La Montagnarde	BH	Airs and Dances, Bk. I (Dorolle)

Composer	Title	Publisher	Volume or Collection
MOZART, L. (1719-1785)	Angloise	Sch	Notebook for Wolfgang (No. 19)
	Aria	Sch	Notebook for Wolfgang (No. 21)
	Bourrée in E Minor	Sch	Notebook for Wolfgang (No. 11)
	Bourrée in D Minor	O	Piano Music for Young Wolfgang (No. 6)
	Burlesque	Sch	Notebook for Wolfgang (No. 3)
		O	Piano Music for Young Wolfgang (No. 3)
		He	A Little Treasury of Classics, Bk. II (Lambert)
	Entrée	Sch	Notebook for Wolfgang (No. 10)
		O	Piano Music for Young Wolfgang (No. 5)
	Eight Minuetts	Sch	Notebook for Nannerl Mozart
	Fantasia in D	O	Piano Music for Young Wolfgang (No. 9)
	March in F	Sch	Notebook for Nannerl Mozart
	Menuets in C	Sch	Notebook for Wolfgang (Nos. 1, 8, 16)
	Menuets in D	Sch	Notebook for Wolfgang (Nos. 7, 13)
	Menuets in D Minor	O	Piano Music for Young Wolfgang (Nos. 2, 4)
	Menuet in F	Sch	Notebook for Nannerl Mozart (No. 12)
	Musette in C	Sch	Notebook for Wolfgang (No. 14)
		O	Piano Music for Young Wolfgang (No. 8)
	Polonaise in C	O	Piano Music for Young Wolfgang (No. 1)
	Polonaise in C	Sch	Notebook for Wolfgang (No. 6)
	Polonaise in D	Sch	Notebook for Wolfgang (No. 4)
	Sarabande in D	Sch	Notebook for Wolfgang (No. 17)
	Schwaben-Tanz	Sch	Notebook for Wolfgang (No. 12)
	Tempo di Marcia	O	Piano Music for Young Wolfgang (No. 12)
	Waldhorn-Stück	Sch	Notebook for Wolfgang (No. 9)
MOZART, W. (1756-1791)	Adagio in D	Sch	A Little Book of Easy Dances (Rehberg)
	Air in A-flat	Sch	The Young Mozart
		H	Easiest Original Pieces
	Air in E-flat	Sch	The Young Mozart
		H	Easiest Original Pieces
	Allegretto in F	Sch	The Young Mozart
	Allegro in B-flat (K 3)	Sch	The Young Mozart
		BMC	Mozart's First Five Compositions
		GS	Master Series for the Young
		He	A Treasury of Easy Classics (Abrams)
		Su	Recital Repertoire, Bk. I (Podolsky)
		K	Mozart, Easy Compositions for Piano
		He	A Treasury of Easy Classics (Abrams)
	Andante in E-flat	Sch	The Young Mozart
		K	Mozart, Easy Compositions for Piano (No. 8)

Composer	Title	Publisher	Volume or Collection
MOZART, W. (cont.)		H	Easiest Original Pieces (No. 2)
	Kontretanz in G	Sch	The Young Mozart
	Menuet in C	BH	Airs and Dances, Bk. I (Dorolle)
	Menuett in B-flat	H	Easiest Original Pieces
		K	Mozart, Easy Compositions for Piano
		Sch	The Young Mozart
	Menuett in C (K 6)	Sch	Notebook for Nannerl Mozart
	Menuett in D (K 7)	Sch	Notebook for Nannerl Mozart
	Menuett in F (K 2)	BMC	Mozart, First Five Compositions
		Sch	The Young Mozart
		K	Mozart, Easy Compositions for Piano
		H	Easiest Original Pieces
		PP	Hundred Best Short Classics, Bk. I
		K	Easy Compositions by Mozart and Beethoven
		GS	Master Series for the Young
	Menuett in F (K 6)	Sch	Notebook for Nannerl Mozart
	Menuett in F	K	Mozart, Easy Compositions For Piano
		Sch	The Young Mozart (pg. 11)
	Menuett in F (K 5)	He	A Treasury of Easy Classics (Abrams)
		K	Mozart, Easy Compositions for Piano (No. 7)
		BMC	Mozart, First Five Compositions
		Sch	The Young Mozart (pg. 16)
	Menuett in G (K 1)	K	Easy Compositions by Mozart and Beethoven
		GS	Master Series for the Young
		K	Mozart, Easy Compositions for Piano
		BMC	Mozart, First Five Compositions
		Su	Recital Repertoire, Bk. I (Podolsky)
		Sch	The Young Mozart
	Passepied	Sch	A Little Book of Easy Dances (Rehberg)
MÜLLER, A. (1767-1817)	Allegro-Stücke	P	Sonatinen Vorstufe (Preparatory Sonatina Album) (No. 4)
	Andante-Stücke		(No. 1)
	Andantino		(No. 5)
	Scherzo		(No. 6)
NEEFE, C. G. (1748-1798)	Allegretto in C	Sch	Clavierstücke für Anfänger
	Minuetto in C		
	Scherzo in E-flat		
NICHELMANN, C. (1717-1762)	Menuetto I in G	Sch	Clavierstücke für Anfänger
	Menuetto II in G Minor		
PURCELL, D. (1660-1717)	Hornpipe in D Minor	H	Contemporaries of Purcell

Composer	Title	Publisher	Volume or Collection
PURCELL, H. (1658-1695)	Ayre in D Minor	He	A Little Treasury of Classics, Bk. I (Lambert)
		PP	The Fredrick Moore Collection Published Separately
	Irish Tune	BMC	Purcell-Arne Album
	March in C, No. I		
	March in C, No. 9 (From Suite 5)		
	Menuet in F	BH	Airs and Dances, Bk. I
	Prelude in G (From Suite I)	A	Beringer's School of Easy Classics: Old English and French Masters
		BMC	Purcell-Arne Album
		He	A Little Treasury of Classics, Bk. III (Lambert)
	Scotch Tune	BMC	Purcell-Arne Album
	Song Tune		
	Trumpet Tune, No. 1	GS	Introduction to Piano Classics, Vol. I (Mirovitch)
REINECKE, K. (1774-1820)	Serenade, Op. 183 Gavotte Lied Praeludium	P	Sonatinen Vorstufe (Preparatory Sonatina Album)
ROUSSEAU, J. (1712-1778)	Le Devin du Village	BH	Airs and Dances, Bk. I (Dorolle)
SCARLATTI, A. (1659-1725)	Aria (From Toccata Seconda)	GS	Introduction to Piano Classics, Vol. I (Mirovitch)
	Minuet in E Minor (From Toccata Quarta)		
SCHALE, C. F. (1713-1800)	Minuetto I in C	Sch	Clavierstücke für Anfänger
	Minuetto II in C Minor		
	Polonaise in C		
SOLER, A. (1729-1783)	Allegretto in D Minor	BH	Airs and Dances, Bk. I (Dorolle)
TÜRK, D. G. (TUERK) (1750-1813)	Arioso in F	Sch	Clavierstücke für Anfänger
	Eighteen Selected Pieces 5. Syncopation 6. Swinging 7. The Trill 8. A Ballet Step 9. Ties 10. Frolic 11. A Grey Cloud 12. A Song-Story 13. Waltz 14. Gavotte	K	Türk, 49 Pieces for Beginners at the Piano

Composer	Title	Publisher	Volume or Collection
TÜRK, D. G. (cont.)	15. At Evening 16. Neighbors 17. Miniature Rondo 18. The Horn with Echo 19. Gentleness 20. The Chase 21. A Regal Dance 22. Joke		

	Four Pieces for Beginners
	  1. Minuet
	  2. March
	  3. Two Melodies
	  4. The Ladder
		He	A Little Treasury of Classics, Bk. I (Lambert)
			Türk, 49 Pieces for Beginners

UHDE, J. O. (1725-1766)	Minuetto in B-flat Minuetto in G	Sch	Clavierstücke für Anfänger
WAGENSEIL, G. (1715-1777)	Menuett in C Scherzo	U Sch	Grosse Meister für kleine Hände Notebook for Nannerl Mozart
WITTHAUER, J. G. (1750-1802)	Allegretto in F Allegretto in F Gavotte	Sch	Clavierstücke für Anfänger (No. 3) (No. 8) (No. 1)
YOUNG, A. (18th cen.)	The Prince's March	BH Su	Old English Worthies (Rowley) Recital Repertoire, Bk. I (Podolsky)

Composer	Title	Publisher	Volume or Collection
ANDRÉ, J. A. (1832-1882)	Sonatine in C	He	A Little Treasury of Sonatinas, Bk. I (Lambert)
BEETHOVEN, L. van (1770-1827)	Ecossaise in E flat (Schottish)	Sch	Kleine Tänze (Frey)
		He	A Treasury of Easy Classics (Abrams)
		BMC	Classical Album of Original Piano Pieces
		PP	Hundred Best Short Classics, Bk. I
	Ecossaise in G (Schottish)	Sch	Kleine Tänze (Frey) (No. 2)
		BMC	Classical Album of Original Piano Pieces
	Russian Folk Song	BMC	Classical Album of Original Piano Pieces
		He	A Little Treasury of Classics, Bk. I (Lambert)
	Two Country Dances	Sch	Kleine Tänze (Frey) (No. 1)
BERTINI, D. (1798-1876)	Menuetto in G (From "Petits Morceaux")	P	Sonatinen Vorstufe (Preparatory Sonatina Album)
BURGMÜLLER, N. (1810-1836)	Ave Maria	GS	Twenty-five Easy and Progressive Studies, Op. 100
		P	
		CF	Road to Piano Artistry, Vol. II (Scionti)
	Ballade	GS	Twenty-five Easy and Progressive Studies, Op. 100
		P	
		He	A Little Treasury of Classics, Bk. III (Lambert)
	Barcarolle	GS	Twenty-five Easy and Progressive Studies, Op. 100
		P	
	Consolation		
	Douce Plainte (Tender Grieving)		
	Inquietude		
	Innocence		
	L'Arabesque		
	La Babillarde (The Chatterbox)		
	La Bergeronnette (The Wagtail)		
	La Chasse (The Chase)		
	La Gracieuse (Grace)		

Composer	Title	Publisher	Volume or Collection
BURGMÜLLER, N. (cont.)	La Tarantelle		
	Le Courant limpide (The Limpid Stream)		
	L'Harmonie des Anges (Harmony of the Angels)	GS	Twenty-five Easy and Progressive Studies, Op. 100
		P	
		CF	Road to Piano Artistry, Vol. II (Scionti)
	L'Hirondelle (The Swallow)	GS	Twenty-five Easy and Progressive Studies, Op. 100
		P	
	Progrés		
	Tendre Fleur (Tender Blossom)		
CLEMENTI, M. (1752-1832)	Spiritoso, From Sonatina Op. 36, No. 1	GS	Clementi: Six Sonatinas, Op. 36
		GS	Thirty-two Sonatinas and Rondos
		P	Album of Sonatinas
		GS	Album of Sonatinas
	Un poco Adagio, From Sonatina Op. 36, No. 3		
GURLITT, C. (1820-1901)	From "Album Leaves," Op. 101 1. March 3. The Sunshiny Morning 4. Northern Strains 5. By the Spring 6. Slumber Song 7. Lament 8. The Fair 9. Turkish March 10. Song without Words 11. Waltz 12. The Little Wanderer 13. Grandfather's Birthday 16. Scherzo 17. Free Fancies 18. Sunday 19. Hunting Song 20. Salto Mortale	GS	Album Leaves for the Young, Op. 101
	A Little Dance, Op. 130, No. 11	GS	Selected Piano Solos by Romantic Composers, Bk. I
	March of the Tin Soldiers, Op. 130, No. 6		
	Melodious Studies, Op. 131 1. Cheerily, Oh! 2. Undaunted 3. Joyous and Mirthful 5. Through Mountain and Valley 6. Scherzo	GS	Twenty-four Melodious Studies, Op. 131

Composer	Title	Publisher	Volume or Collection
GURLITT, C. (cont.)	Prayer, Op. 130, No. 4	GS	Selected Piano Solos by Romantic Composers, Bk. I
	Serious Moments, Op. 130, No. 23		
	The Fair, Op. 101, No. 8		
	Waltz, Op. 101, No. 11		
HASSLINGER, K. (1816-1868)	Sonatine in C	He	Little Treasury of Sonatinas, Bk. I
HELLER, S. (1813-1888)	L'Avalanche, Op. 45, No. 2	R GS GS GS	Twenty-five Studies for Piano, Op. 45 Fifty Selected Studies, No. 16 Published Separately
	The Coquette, Op. 47, No. 3	R GS GS	Twenty-five Studies for Piano, Op. 47 Fifty Selected Studies (No. 2)
SCHUMANN, R. (1810-1856)	Bagatelle, Op. 68, No. 5 (Little Piece)	P GS GS	Album for the Young, Op. 68 Master Series for the Young
	Choral, Op. 68, No. 4	P GS GS	Album for the Young, Op. 68 Selected Piano Solos by Romantic Composers, Bk. I
	Ditty, Op. 68, No. 3 (Humming Song)	P GS GS GS	Album for the Young, Op. 68 Selected Piano Solos by Romantic Composers, Bk. I Master Series for the Young
	Melody, Op. 68, No. 1	P GS GS PP GS A	Album for the Young, Op. 68 Master Series for the Young Hundred Best Short Classics, Bk. I Selected Piano Solos by Romantic Composers, Bk. I Beringer's School of Easy Classics: Schumann
	Soldier's March, Op. 68 No. 2	P GS GS PP He P He	Album for the Young, Op. 68 Master Series for the Young Hundred Best Short Classics, Bk. I A Little Treasury of Classics, Bk. II (Lambert) Sonatinen Vorstufe A Treasury of Easy Classics (Abrams)
	The Merry Farmer's Return from Work, Op. 68, No. 10 (The Merry Peasant)	P GS GS PP A	Album for the Young, Op. 68 Master Series for the Young Hundred Best Short Classics, Bk. I Beringer's School of Easy Classics: Schumann

Composer	Title	Publisher	Volume or Collection
SCHUMANN, R. (cont.)		P	Sonatinen Vorstufe
		He	A Treasury of Easy Classics (Abrams)
TSCHAIKOWSKY, P. (1840-1893)	Old French Song, Op. 39, No. 16	GS	Master Series for the Young
	The Doll's Burial, Op. 39 No. 7	GS	Album for the Young, Op. 39
	The Sick Doll, Op. 39, No. 6		
WEBER, C. (1786-1826)	Ecossaise in F	He	A Little Treasury of Classics, Bk. I (Lambert)
	Ecossaise in G		

Composer	Title	Publisher	Volume or Collection
BARTÓK, BÉLA (1881-1945)	Allegro ironico (Jeering Song)	Sch BH L K	The New Piano Book, I For Children, Vol. I 42 Hungarian Folk Melodies Piano Pieces for Children, Vol. II
	Eighteen Elementary Pieces	K	The First Term at the Piano
	Folksong	Sch K	The New Piano Book, II Ten Easy Pieces for Children
	(Poco Andante)	I	16 Pieces for Children (No. 3)
	From "For Children," Vol. I, Nos. 1-11; 13-20; 22, 24, 25, 27, 29, 30, 31, 34	BH	For Children, Vol. I
	From "For Children," Vol. II, Nos. 1-10; 12-17; 19, 20, 23, 24, 28, 30, 31, 32, 35, 38	BH	For Children, Vol. II
	From "Hungarian Folk Melodies", Nos. 1-11; 13-20; 22, 24, 25, 27, 29, 32, 33, 36	L	42 Hungarian Folk Melodies (Same contents as "For Children," Vol. I except Nos. 25 and 31)
	From "Little Pieces for Children", Nos. 1-11; 13-20, 21	K	Little Pieces for Children, Vol. I (Same contents as "42 Hungarian Folk Melodies" Nos. 1-22, and "For Children, Vol. I")
	In Yugoslav Mode	BH	Mikrokosmos, Vol. II
	Meditation		
	Minuetto		
	Not Too Fast	MMC	Meet Modern Music, Part I
	Peasant's Song	MMC K I	Meet Modern Music, Part I Ten Easy Pieces for Children 16 Pieces for Children
	From "Piano Pieces for Children", Nos. 24, 25, 27, 29, 32, 33, 36	K	Piano Pieces for Children, Vol. II (Same contents as 42 Hungarian Folk Melodies, Nos. 23-42).
	From "Sixteen Pieces for Children", Nos. 1-8; 12-15	I	16 Pieces for Children (Contents selected from "For Children, Vol. I" and "Ten Easy Pieces for Children")
	Song of the Tramp	MMC BH	Meet Modern Music, Part I For Children, Vol. II (No. 7)
	Dance of the Slovaks	K	Ten Easy Pieces for Children
	Folksong		
	Peasant's Song		
	The Bagpipe	Sch	The New Piano Book, Vol. I

Composer	Title	Publisher	Volume or Collection
BLANCHET, E. (1877-1943)	"L'Album de Nanette" 1st Series 1. Premier Pas 2. Cloches Joyeuses 3. Petite Romance 2nd Series 1. Monsieur Polichinelle 2. Il Etait une Bergère 3. Nous n'irons plus au-bois	E	L'Album de Nanette
BOWLES, PAUL (1910-)	"Folk Preludes" 1. Peter Gray 2. Ching A Ring Chaw 4. Oh! Potatoes They Grow Small Over There	MMC	Folk Preludes
DIAMOND, DAVID (1915-)	Eight Piano Pieces 1. Pease-Porridge Hot 2. Jumping Jacks 3. The Old Mr. Turtle 4. Handy-Spandy, Jack- A-Dandy 5. Jack and Jill 6. Rock-A-Bye, Baby 7. Little Jumping Joan 8. Lullaby	GS	Eight Piano Pieces
DROSDOFF, A. (1889-)	Ukranian Song	W	Modern Russian Piano Music By Contemporary Composers
FREED, ISADORE (1900-)	Around the Maypole Punchinello Story at Evening	CF	Masters of Our Day
GOEDICKE, ALEXANDER (1877-)	Hopak In India Marlborough Goes to Work	L	The Student Pianist, Vol. I (Mirovitch)
GRETCHANINOFF, ALEXANDER (1864-)	Album d'Andrucha, Op. 133 1. Old Children's Song 2. Little Dreamer 3. Naughty Girl 4. Little Elegant 5. The Dance of the Goldfishes 6. The Mountebank 7. Gallant Cavalier 8. My Little Dog Joujou 9. Invitation to a Walk 10. Children's Dance	E	Album d'Andrucha, Op. 133
	Children's Book, Op. 98 1. Fairy Tale 2. The Tin Soldiers in Camp	Sch	Children's Book, Op. 98

Composer	Title	Publisher	Volume or Collection
GRETCHANINOFF, ALEXANDER (cont.)	3. The Tin Soldiers Marching 4. Farewell 5. Riding the Hobby-Horse 6. In the Woodland Glade 7. Njanja Being Ill 8. A Tiresome Lesson 9. Cradle Song 10. A Little Dance 11. A Terrible Event 12. A Study 13. After the Ball 14. The Little Traveller 15. The Little Would-Be Man		
	Four Pieces From ''Album de Nina,'' Op. 141 1. Reve d'Enfant 3. Après La Messe 7. Au Rouet 9. Nuages Du Soir	E	Album de Nina, Op. 141
	Four Pieces From ''A Child's Day,'' Op. 109 1. Morning Prayer 2. At Work 3. My Little Horse 4. The Broken Toy	Sch	A Child's Day, Op. 109
	Glass Beads, Op. 123 1. Morning Walk 2. Little Beggar 3. Etude 4. Sad Song 5. On the Bicycle 6. Waltz 7. Heavy Work 8. My First Ball 9. Complaint 10. In the Fields 11. Mother's Caress 12. On the Harmonica	K	Glass Beads, Op. 123
	Twelve Little Sketches, Op. 182 1. Sunrise 2. With the Fishing Rod 3. Returning Home with a Bouquet of Flowers 4. The Orphan 5. A New Friend 6. On the Swing 7. At Grandmother's 8. Country Lad 9. Asking for a New Doll	I	Twelve Little Sketches For Children, Op. 182

Composer	Title	Publisher	Volume or Collection
GRETCHANINOFF, ALEXANDER (cont.)	10. The New Doll 11. Tag 12. It's Time to Go Home		
JACOBI, FREDERICK (1891-1952)	Once Upon A Time	CF	Masters of Our Day
KABALEVSKY, DMITRI (1904-)	A Little Song	L I	15 Pieces for Children, Op. 27, Bk. I 18 Pieces for Children, Op. 27
	Country Dance, Op. 34, No. 17	L	The Student Pianist, Vol. I (Mirovitch)
	Little Pieces for Children, Op. 39, Nos. 1-20	I	24 Little Pieces for Children, Op. 39
	Moonlight on the River	I	18 Pieces for Children, Op. 27
	Playing Ball	L I	15 Pieces for Children, Op. 27, Bk. I 18 Pieces for Children, Op. 27
	Running Along, Op. 39, No. 6	L	The Student Pianist, Vol. I (Mirovitch)
	Singing, Op. 39, No. 8		
	The Little Twins, Op. 39, No. 7		

KODÁLY, ZOLTÁN (1882-)	Children's Dances
	  1. Allegretto
	  2. Allegretto Cantabile
	  3. Vivace
		BH	Children's Dances

MAYKAPAR, SAMUEL (1867-)	Piece Enfantine, Op. 4, No. 3	Su	Recital Repertoire, Bk. II (Podolsky)
MIASKOWSKY, NICOLAI (1881-1951)	Carefree	W	Modern Russian Piano Music
MILHAUD, DARIUS (1892-)	Touches Blanches Touches Noires	CF	Masters of Our Day
MOORE, DOUGLAS (1893-)	Fiddlin' Joe Grievin' Annie	CF	Masters of Our Day
PAZ, JUAN (1897-)	Pampeana	CF	Masters of Our Day
REBIKOV, VLADIMIR (1866-1920)	Accompanimento ostinato	Sch	Piano Album, No. II (Rowley)
	A Little Girl Pleading with her Mother (Une Fillette Implore Sa Mère)	I Sch	Pictures for Children, Op. 37 Piano Album No. II (Rowley)
	Languorous Dance		
	Persuasion		
	The Bear		

Composer	Title	Publisher	Volume or Collection
REVUELTAS, SILVESTRE (1899-1940)	Canción	CF	Masters of Our Day
RHENE-BATON, (1879-1940)	Une petite chanson (A Little Song)	E E MMC	Pour Yvonne Published Separately Meet Modern Music, Part I
	Une petite gavotte	E E	Pour Yvonne Published Separately
	Une petite valse	E E MMC	Pour Yvonne Published Separately Meet Modern Music, Part I

ROBB, J. D. (1892-)	Pictures of New Mexico
	  In the Cottonwood Grove
	  In the Indian Village
	  Siesta Time
	  The Bells of the Mission
		AMP	Published Separately

RUBINSTEIN, BERYL (1898-1953)	Tally-Ho Wildflowers Butterflies	CF	A Day in the Country

	Musical Fancies, Series I
	  1. The Cuckoo
	  2. Valse
	  3. Gavotte
	  4. Song without Words
	  5. Puck
		CF	Published Separately

SAMINSKY, LAZARE (1882-)	Old Veranda, Op. 45, No. 1 from "Cynthia's Playnook"	CF	Masters of Our Day
SATIE, ERIK (1866-1925)	Petit prélude à la journée Berceuse Marche du grand escalier	E	Enfantillages pittoresques

	Menus propos Enfantine
	  1. Chant guerrier du roi des hericots (War Song of the Bean King)
	  2. Ce que Dit la Petite Princesse des Tulips (The Tulip Princess Says)
	  3. Valse du Chocolat aux Amandes (Waltz of the Chocolate Bar)
		E
		MMC
			Menus propos Enfantines
			Meet Modern Music, Part I

SHOSTAKOVITCH, DMITRI (1906-)	Children's Pieces
	  1. March
	  2. Waltz
	  3. The Bear
	  4. A Happy Fairy Tale
		L	Six Children's Pieces
			
			Published Separately

Composer	Title	Publisher	Volume or Collection
SHOSTAKOVITCH, DMITRI (cont.)	5. A Sad Fairy Tale 6. The Mechanical Doll		Published Separately
STRAVINSKY, IGOR (1882-)	Andantino (Just Walking)	O MMC	The Five Fingers Meet Modern Music, Part I
TANSMAN, ALEXANDRE (1897-)	Melody	L L	Children at Play Published Separately

	From "Pour les Enfants," First Set
	  5. Valse des marionettes
	  7. Dresden China Figures
	  8. Vacation is over
	 10. The Firemen
	 12. Conclusion
		AMP	Pour les Enfants, First Set

	From "Pour les Enfants," Second Set
	  1. Stroll
	  2. In the Garden
	  3. Mazurka
	  4. The Arithmetic Lesson
	  6. Solemn Occasion
		AMP	Pour les Enfants, Second Set

SECTION II

UPPER ELEMENTARY

GRADES III AND IV

MUSIC OF THE SIXTEENTH, SEVENTEENTH AND EIGHTEENTH CENTURIES

Composer	Title	Publisher	Volume or Collection
ARNE, T. A. (1710-1778)	Country Dance	BMC	Purcell-Arne Album
	Figure Dance		
	Jig		
	March from "Alfred"		
	Minuet in G		
	Sailor's Dance		
	Siciliano		
BACH, C. P. E. (1714-1788)	Allegro in A Minor	K	The Direct Path (Hermann)
	Allegro in C Minor	C	Eighteenth Century Music, Vol. I
	Allegro in D	H	The Sons of Johann Sebastian Bach
	Allegro in D	C	Eighteenth Century Music, Vol. II
	Allegro in E-flat	H	The Sons of Johann Sebastian Bach
	Allegro in G	H	The Sons of Johann Sebastian Bach
	La Caroline	H Su	The Sons of Johann Sebastian Bach Recital Repertoire, Bk. I (Podolsky)
	La Xenophone	SG	Classics from the Seventeenth and Eighteenth Centuries (Tapper)
	Little Fantasy in D Minor	U	Old Masters for Young Pianists (Kuranda)
	Minuet in G	C	Eighteenth Century Music, Vol. II (No. 3)
	Solfeggietto	He B CF Sch GS K	A Treasury of Easy Classics (Abrams) Hours with the Masters, Bk. V Road to Piano Artistry, Vol. VI (Scionti) Die Söhne Bach Published Separately Published Separately
BACH, J. C. F. (1732-1795)	Angloise	Sch	Clavierstücke für Anfänger
	Minuet to Dance in D	Sch H	Menuetten fürs Clavier The Sons of Johann Sebastian Bach
	Schwaebisch in F	Sch	Clavierstücke für Anfänger
BACH, J. S. (1685-1750)	Aria, "Gedenke doch mein Geist" (Pray, Remember My Soul)	BMC K GS	Bach for Early Grades, Bk. II Little Notebook for Anna Magdalena Bach (pg. 119) Master Series for the Young (pg. 5)
	Bourrée in A	K	The First Bach Book
	Bourrée in B Minor	B	Hours with the Masters, Bk. III
	Bourrée in E Minor	GS	First Lessons in Bach, Bk. I (Carroll)

Composer	Title	Publisher	Volume or Collection
BACH, J. S. (cont.)		CF	Bach First Lessons, Bk. I (Carroll)
		GS	Master Series for the Young
		K	The First Bach Book
		CF	Road to Piano Artistry, Vol. II (Scionti)
	Chorale, ''Schaff's mit mir, Gott'' (Do As Thou Wills't with Me O Lord)	K	Little Notebook of Anna Magdalena Bach
	Gavotte in G Minor	GS	First Lessons in Bach, Bk. I (Carroll)
		CF	Bach First Lessons, Bk. I (Carroll)
		PP	Hundred Best Short Classics, Bk. I
		B	Hours with the Masters, Bk. III
	Little Prelude in C	BMC	Bach for Early Grades, Bk. II (No. 18)
		GS	Eighteen Little Preludes and Fugues (No. 15)
		Sch	Little Piano Book of Wilhelm Friedemann Bach (No. 2)
		GS	Master Series for the Young (pg. 19)
		GS	Short Preludes and Fuges (No. 1)
		K	The First Bach Book (No. 18)
		K	Various Short Preludes and Fuges (No. 1)
	Little Prelude in C	GS	Eighteen Little Preludes and Fugues (No. 9)
		K	First Bach Book (No. 19)
		Sch	Little Piano Book of Wilhelm Friedemann Bach
		GS	Master Series for the Young (pg. 14)
		U	Old Masters for Young Pianists (Kuranda)
		GS	Short Preludes and Fugues (No. 2)
		K	Various Short Preludes and Fugues (No. 2)
	Little Prelude in C Minor	GS	Eighteen Little Preludes and Fugues (No. 4)
		K	First Bach Book (No. 21)
		GS	Master Series for the Young (pg. 15)
		CF	Road to Piano Artistry, Vol. II (pg. 8)
		GS	Short Preludes and Fugues (No. 3)
		K	Various Short Preludes and Fugues (No. 3)
	March in D	CF	Bach First Lessons, Bk. I (Carroll)
		BMC	Bach for Early Grades, Bk. I
		GS	First Lessons in Bach, Bk. I (Carroll)
		PP	Hundred Best Short Classics, Bk. I
		K	Little Notebook for Anna Magdalena Bach, (pg. 60)
		GS	Master Series for the Young
		P	Notenbuch der Anna Magdalena Bach
		K	The First Bach Book
	March in E-flat	BMC	Bach for Early Grades, Bk. II (In C Major)
		K	Little Notebook for Anna Magdalena Bach
		GS	Master Series for the Young
		P	Notenbuch der Anna Magdalena Bach
		K	The First Bach Book

Composer	Title	Publisher	Volume or Collection
BACH, J. S. (cont.)	March in G	CF	Bach First Lessons, Bk. I (Carroll)
		BMC	Bach for Early Grades, Bk. I
		GS	First Lessons in Bach, Bk. I (Carroll)
		K	Little Notebook for Anna Magdalena Bach
		P	Notenbuch der Anna Magdalena Bach
		K	The First Bach Book
	Menuet in A Minor	K	Little Notebook for Anna Magdalena Bach (pg. 58)
		P	Notenbuch der Anna Magdalena Bach
		I	The Little Music Book for Anna Magdalena Bach
	Menuet in B-flat	K	The Little Notebook for Anna Magdalena Bach (pg. 53)
		K	The First Bach Book
	Menuet in C Minor	BMC	Bach for Early Grades, Bk. I
		CF	Bach First Lessons, Bk. I (Carroll)
		GS	First Lessons in Bach, Bk. I (Carroll)
		K	The Little Notebook for Anna Magdalena Bach
		K	The First Bach Book
	Menuet in E	CF	Bach First Lessons, Bk. II (Carroll)
		GS	First Lessons in Bach, Bk. II (Carroll)
		K	French Suites, No. 6 in E
		P	French Suites
		GS	French Suites
		GS	Master Series for the Young
		U	Old Masters for Young Pianists (Kuranda)
	Menuet in F	K	Little Notebook for Anna Magdalena Bach (pg. 42)
		P	Notenbuch der Anna Magdalena Bach
		K	The First Bach Book
		I	The Little Music Book for Anna Magdalena Bach
	Menuet in F	CF	Bach First Lessons, Bk. II (Carroll)
		GS	First Lessons in Bach, Bk. II (Carroll)
	Menuet in G	BMC	Bach for Early Grades, Bk. II
	Menuet in G (I)	Sch	Little Piano Book for Wilhelm Friedemann Bach
		CF	Road to Piano Artistry, Vol. III (Scionti)
	Menuet in G (III)	Sch	Little Piano Book for Wilhelm Friedemann Bach
	Menuet in G Minor (II)	BMC	Bach for Early Grades, Bk. II
		Sch	Little Piano Book for Wilhelm Friedemann Bach
		K	The First Bach Book (pg. 12)
	Menuet in G Minor	Sch	Little Piano Book for Wilhelm Friedemann Bach (pg. 9)
	Polonaise in D Minor	BMC	Bach for Early Grades, Bk. II
		K	Little Notebook for Anna Magdalena Bach (pg. 74)
		P	Notenbuch der Anna Magdalena Bach (pg. 15)

Composer	Title	Publisher	Volume or Collection
BACH, J. S. (cont.)	Polonaise in G	CF	Bach First Lessons, Bk. II (Carroll)
		GS	First Lessons in Bach, Bk. II (Carroll)
		K	Little Notebook for Anna Magdalena Bach (pg. 82)
		P	Notenbuch der Anna Magdalena Bach (pg. 18)
	Prelude in C	BMC	Bach for Early Grades, Bk. III (pg. 4)
		K	Little Notebook for Anna Magdalena Bach (pg. 84)
		GS	Master Series for the Young (pg. 22)
		PP	Hundred Best Short Classics, Bk. II
		K	Well Tempered Clavier, Bk. I (No. 1)
	Prelude in E Minor	BMC	Bach for Early Grades, Bk. II
BACH, W. F. (1710-1784)	Minuet in G	CF	Road to Piano Artistry, Vol. I (Scionti)
BARRETT, J. (1674-1735 or 1736)	Hornpipe (The St. Catherine)	H	Contemporaries of Purcell
		BH	Old English Worthies
		Su	Recital Repertoire, Bk. I (Podolsky)
BENDA, F. (1709-1786)	Minuet in G	Sch	Menuetten fürs Clavier
BLOW, J. (1649-1708)	Theatre Tune	H	Contemporaries of Purcell
BYRD, W. (1542-1623)	Rowland	BH	Airs and Dances, Bk. I (Dorolle)
CLARKE, J. (1670-1707)	An Ayre in G	BH	Early English Keyboard Music
	Ayre in C	H	Contemporaries of Purcell
	March in D	BH	Early English Keyboard Music
CLÉRAMBAULT, L. (1676-1749)	Allegro in D Minor	BH	Airs and Dances, Bk. I (Dorolle)
CORELLI, A. (1653-1713)	Allegro vivace	BH	Airs and Dances, Bk. II (Dorolle)
	Sarabande in G	P	Sonatinen Vorstufe (Preparatory Sonatina Album)
COUPERIN, F. (1668-1733)	Bourdon	BH	Airs and Dances, Bk. I (Dorolle)
	Fanfare in D	U	Old Masters for Young Pianists (Kuranda)
	Les Coucous	BH	Airs and Dances, Bk. II (Dorolle)
	Le Dodo	BH	Airs and Dances, Bk. I (Dorolle)
	L'Epineuse	BH	Airs and Dances, Bk. I (Dorolle)
	Le Petit Rien	PP	Hundred Best Short Classics, Bk. I
		SG	Classics from the Seventeenth and Eighteenth Centuries
		He	A Treasury of Easy Classics (Abrams)
	Passepied in D	BH	Airs and Dances, Bk. I (Dorolle)

Composer	Title	Publisher	Volume or Collection
COUPERIN, F. (cont.)	The Knitters	U	Old Masters for Young Pianists (Kuranda)
DANDRIEU, de (1684-1740)	The Fifers	BH	Airs and Dances, Bk. I (Dorolle)
		SG	Classics from the Seventeenth and Eighteenth Centuries
DAQUIN, C. (1694-1772)	Tambourin	He	A Little Treasury of Classics, Bk. II (Lambert)
DUSSEK, J. (1760-1812)	Minuetto in G	B	Hours with the Masters, Bk. III
	Menuett with Variation	P	Sonatinen Vorstufe (Preparatory Sonatina Album)
FARNABY, G. (1565-1600)	A Toye	Su	Recital Repertoire, Bk. I (Podolsky)
		He	A Little Treasury of Classics, Bk. II (Lambert)
FISCHER, J. K. F. (1650-1746)	Bourrée in A Minor	GS	Introduction to Piano Classics, Vol. I (Mirovitch)
	Fugue in C	K	A Little Book of Fugues
	From "The Notebook" Bourrée in F Marche de Landau Menuet in A Minor Menuet in A Minor Menuet in C Menuet in F Menuet in G Sarabande in A Minor	Sch	The Notebook of Johann Kaspar Ferd. Fischer (No. 15) (No. 9) (No. 11) (No. 13)
GLÄSER, C. L. T. (1747-1797)	Angloise in F Minuetto in B-flat Minuetto in F	Sch	Clavierstücke für Anfänger
GRAUPNER, C. (1683-1760)	Air (From Suite in G) Air en Gavotte in C Gavotte in G Menuett in D Menuett (From Suite in F)	P	Contemporaries of Telemann
GROSSE, M. C. (2nd Half of 18th Century)	Minuetto I in G Minuetto II in G Minor	Sch	Menuetten fürs Clavier
GRÜNWALD, G. (1673-1739)	Gavotte in C Menuett I and II in A Minor Menuett (From Partita in G) Sarabande in A Minor	P	Contemporaries of Telemann

Composer	Title	Publisher	Volume or Collection
HANDEL, G. F. (1685-1759)	Air in B-flat	Sch Sch	Aylesford Pieces (No. 13) Pieces for Harpsichord, Vol. II (No. 39)
	Bourrée in D Minor	Sch	Twenty Little Dances
	Bourrée in G		
	Bourrée in G Minor		
	Gavotte in G	He Sch	A Little Treasury of Classics, Bk. II (Lambert) Twenty Little Dances (Rigaudon, No. 15)
	Marsch in D	Sch	Twenty Little Dances
	Menuet in A Minor	Sch Sch	Pieces for Harpsichord, Vol. I (No. 8) Aylesford Pieces (No. 19)
	Menuet in B Minor	Sch	Pieces for Harpsichord, Vol. II (No. 71)
	Menuet in B-flat	Sch Sch	Twenty Little Dances, Vol. II (No. 14) Pieces for Harpsichord, Vol. II (No. 66)
	Menuet in D	Sch Sch	Aylesford Pieces (No. 10) Pieces for Harpsichord, Vol. II (No. 57)
	Menuet in D	Sch	Aylesford Pieces (No. 12) Pieces for Harpsichord, Vol. II (No. 58)
	Menuet in D Minor	Sch Sch	Aylesford Pieces (No. 9) Pieces for Harpsichord, Vol. II (No. 56)
	Menuet in F	Sch	Pieces for Harpsichord, Vol. II (No. 61)
	Menuet in G Minor		(No. 64)
	Menuet in G Minor	Sch	Pieces for Harpsichord, Vol. I (No. 3)
	Menuet in G Minor	Sch	Pieces for Harpsichord, Vol. I (No. 4)
	Menuet in G Minor	Sch	Twenty Little Dances (No. 19)
	Menuetto in D Minor	GS	Twelve Easy Pieces (No. 2)
	Menuetto in F		
	Minuet in A	Sch	Pieces for Harpsichord, Vol. II (No. 69)
	Minuet in A		(No. 70)
	Minuet in B-flat		(No. 72)
	Minuet in B-flat		(No. 73)
	Minuet in B-flat		(No. 74)
	Minuet in B-flat		(No. 75)
	Minuet in F		(No. 62)
	Minuet in F	Sch	Pieces for Harpsichord, Vol. I (No. 14)
	Minuet in G		Pieces for Harpsichord, Vol. II (No. 63)
	Minuet in G		Pieces for Harpsichord, Vol. I (No. 28)
	Minuet in G Minor		(No. 11)
	Passepied in A	Sch Sch	Aylesford Pieces (No. 18) Pieces for Harpsichord, Vol. I (No. 7)
	Passepied in C	Sch	Pieces for Harpsichord, Vol. II (No. 76)

Composer	Title	Publisher	Volume or Collection
HÄSSLER, J. (1747-1822)	Allegro in C	GS	Introduction to Piano Classics, Vol. II (Mirovitch)
		Su	Recital Repertoire, Bk. I (Podolsky)
		Sch	Simple Short Piano Pieces (14a and 14b)
	Minuetto I in C	Sch	Menuetten fürs Clavier
	Minuetto II in C Minor		
	Minuetto in C		
	Minuetto in F		
HAYDN, J. (1732-1809)	Allegretto	K	The Direct Path
	Allegretto risoluto in G	U	Little Dances for Young Folk (No. 2)
	Allegro con brio in D		(No. 3)
	Easy Pieces	K	Twelve Easy Pieces
	1. Andante grazioso		
	2. Allegro		
	3. Andante		
	4. Presto, ma non troppo		
	5. Adagio cantabile		
	6. Vivace		
	7. Allegro		
	8. Andantino, un poco allegretto		
	9. Menuetto		
	10. Menuetto		
	11. Vivace assai		
	12. Andante con moto		
	Menuetten I and II in A-flat	P	Sonatas, Vol. IV (No. 41)
	Menuetto in A	P	Sonatas, Vol. II (No. 23)
	Menuetto in D	AMP	Six Sonatinas (No. 1)
	Menuet in G	AMP	Six Sonatinas (No. 6)
	Menuetto Giocoso in C	GS	Published Separately
		CF	Road to Piano Artistry, Vol. IV (Scionti)
		Su	Recital Repertoire, Bk. I (Podolsky)
	(Allegretto Giocoso)	U	Little Dances for Young Folk (No. 1)
	(Minuet in C)	GS	Master Series for the Young
		He	A Treasury of Easy Classics (Abrams)
	Minuet in B-flat	GS	Introduction to Piano Classics, Vol. I (Mirovitch)
	Minuet in D	P	Sonatas, Vol. II (No. 20)
		GS	Sonatas, Vol. II (No. 19)
		K	Sonatas, Vol. I (No. 19)
		PP	Hundred Best Short Classics, Bk. I
	Romanze in F	P	Sonatinen Vorstufe (Preparatory Sonatina Album)
	Sonatina in C	AMP	Six Sonatinas (No. 2)
		P	Six Little Divertimenti (No. 5)
	Sonatina in G	AMP	Six Sonatinas (No. 3)
		P	Six Little Divertimenti (No. 4)

Composer	Title	Publisher	Volume or Collection
HILLER, J. (1728-1804)	Minuetto II in C	Sch	Simple Short Piano Pieces
	Minuet in F	GS	Introduction to Piano Classics, Vol. II (Mirovitch)
	Musette in C	Sch	Simple Short Piano Pieces (No. 1)
HOOK, J. (1746-1827)	Divertimento No. 1	BH	Early English Keyboard Music
	Giocoso (From Sonatina in G)	He	Little Treasury of Sonatinas, Bk. I
	Sonatina in D Giocoso Menuet Country Dance	BH	Early English Sonatinas
	Sonatina in G Allegro non troppo Rondo pastorale		
KIRNBERGER, J. (1721-1783)	Fughetta in C	Sch	Clavierstücke für Anfänger
	Invention and Little Fugue	GS	Introduction to Piano Classics, Vol. I (Mirovitch)
	Menuet in B-flat	U	Grosse Meister für kleine Hände
	Minuetto in A	Sch	Clavierstücke für Anfänger
	Minuetto in C		
	Minuet in C	GS	Introduction to Piano Classics, Vol. I (Mirovitch)
	Polonaise in E-flat		
KREBS, J. (1713-1780)	Menuett in A Minor	P	Contemporaries of Telemann
	Minuetto in A	Sch	Menuetten fürs Clavier
KUHNAU, J. (1660-1722)	Aria in A	U	Grosse Meister für kleine Hände
	Gavotte in B Minor	GS	Introduction to Piano Classics, Vol. I (Mirovitch)
	Prelude from Partita V in G	U	Grosse Meister für kleine Hände
		GS	Introduction to Piano Classics, Vol. I (Mirovitch)
		K	Old Masters of the 16th, 17th and 18th Centuries
LÉVASSEUR, P. F. (1753- ?)	Rondeau à l'Allemande	P	Sonatinen Vorstufe
LOEILLET, J. (1653-1728)	Cibel	H	Contemporaries of Purcell
	Minuet in E Minor		
MAICHELBECK, F. A. (1702-1750)	Buffone	U	Grosse Meister für kleine Hände
MOZART, L. (1719-1785)	Allegro in A	O	Piano Music for Young Wolfgang (No. 15)
	Allegro in C	Sch	Notebook for Nannerl Mozart (No. 20)

Composer	Title	Publisher	Volume or Collection
MOZART, L. (cont.)	Allegro in G		(No. 11)
	Andante in B-flat		(No. 21)
	Aria in G Minor	O	Piano Music for Young Wolfgang (No. 19)
	Bourrée in C Minor	Sch	Notebook for Wolfgang
		O	Piano Music for Young Wolfgang (No. 13)
	The Hunt	U	Grosse Meister für kleine Hände
	Fantasia in A Minor	O	Piano Music for Young Wolfgang (No. 23)
	Fantasia in D Minor	O	Piano Music for Young Wolfgang (No. 21)
	Gavotte in D	Sch	Notebook for Wolfgang (No. 23)
	Gigue in D	O	Piano Music for Young Wolfgang (No. 22)
	March in C		(No. 11)
	March in D		(No. 16)
	March in F	Sch	Notebook for Wolfgang (No. 30)
		O	Piano Music for Young Wolfgang (No. 14)
	March in F		(No. 18)
	Menuet in A Minor	Sch	Notebook for Wolfgang (No. 26)
	Menuet in B-flat		(No. 22)
	Menuet in C	U	Grosse Meister für kleine Hände
	Menuet in C	Sch	Notebook for Wolfgang (No. 32)
	Menuet in C Minor		(No. 31)
	Menuet in F		(No. 18)
	Passepied in D		(No. 20)
	Polonaise in A		(No. 25)
	Polonaise in C		(No. 15)
	Polonaise in C	O	Piano Music for Young Wolfgang (No. 10)
	Scherzo in C		(No. 20)
	Scherzo in F	Sch	Notebook for Nannerl (No. 13)
MOZART, W. A. (1756-1791)	Adagio in C (From Viennese Sonatina No. 6)	Sch	Viennese Sonatinas
		MMC	
		CF	Road to Piano Artistry, Vol. VI (Scionti)
		K	Easy Compositions of Mozart and Beethoven
	Allegretto in C	Sch	The Young Mozart
	Andante in B-flat		
	Andante in F (K 6)	Sch	Notebook for Nannerl
	Andantino in E-flat (K 236)	GS	Introduction to Piano Classics, Vol. I (Mirovitch)
		He	A Treasury of Easy Classics (Abrams)
	Easy Dances	Sch	A Little Book of Easy Dances
	1. Entrée		
	2. Cache-cache		

Composer	Title	Publisher	Volume or Collection
MOZART, W. A. (cont.)	3. Idyll 4. Gavotte joyeuse 6. Gavotte gracieuse 7. Pantomime 9. Gavotte 10. Finale 11. Minuetto in G 12. Allegro 13. Minuetto in F 14. Andantino 15. Minuetto in F		
	Kontretanz in F	Sch	The Young Mozart
	Menuetto in C (From Viennese Sonatina No. 1)	Sch MMC CF B	Six Viennese Sonatinas Road to Piano Artistry, Vol. III (Scionti) Hours with the Masters, Bk. II
	Menuet in D (K 7)	Sch	Notebook for Nannerl
	Menuet in D (K 94)	K	Easy Compositions of Mozart and Beethoven
	Menuett in F (K 4)	K K BMC Sch He	Easy Compositions of Mozart and Beethoven (No. 3) Mozart, Easy Compositions for Piano (No. 7) Mozart's First Five Compositions Notebook for Nannerl A Treasury of Easy Classics (Abrams)
	Menuett in G	Sch	The Young Mozart (No. 5)
	Presto	K Sch	Mozart, Easy Compositions for Piano (No. 9) The Young Mozart
	Rondo in F		
	Siziliano in D Minor		
	Sonatina in C	He	Little Treasury of Sonatinas, Bk. II
	Waltzes, (K 600, 602, 605)	U P Sch	Twelve Waltzes German Dances Fifteen Waltzes (Frey)
	Three Waltzes (K 600)	PP	Hundred Best Short Classics, Bk. I
MUFFAT, J. T. (1690-1770)	Menuet mit Jagdhörnern	U	Grosse Meister für kleine Hände
MURCHHAUSER, F. (1663-1738)	Christmas Song	He	A Little Treasury of Classics, Bk. I (Lambert)
	Pastoral Air	BH	Airs and Dances, Bk. I (Dorolle)
NEEFE, C. G. (1748-1798)	Arioso in G	Sch GS Su	Simple Short Piano Pieces Introduction to Piano Classics, Bk. I (Mirovitch) Recital Repertoire, Bk. I (Podolsky)
	Minuetto in C	Sch	Menuetten fürs Clavier

Composer	Title	Publisher	Volume or Collection
NICHELMANN, C. (1717-1762)	Polonaise in A	Sch	Clavierstücke für Anfänger
PASQUINI, B. (1637-1710)	Pastorale	BH	Airs and Dances, Bk. I
PURCELL, D. (1660-1717)	Air in D	H	Contemporaries of Purcell
PURCELL, H. (1658-1695)	Gavotte in G	H B	Contemporaries of Purcell Hours with the Masters, Bk. II
	Hornpipe in D (From D Major Suite VI)	BMC	Purcell-Arne Album
	Jig in G Minor	GS	Introduction to Piano Classics, Vol. I (Mirovitch)
	Minuet in G (From Suite in G, No. I)	PP BMC He A	Hundred Best Short Classics, Bk. I Purcell-Arne Album A Little Treasury of Classics, Bk. III (Lambert) Beringer's School of Easy Classics: Old English and French Masters
	Riggadoon (From Suite in C, No. V)	BMC	Purcell-Arne Album
	Siciliano in G Minor (From Suite in G Minor No. II)	BH BMC A	Airs and Dances, Bk. I (Dorolle) Purcell-Arne Album Beringer's School of Easy Classics: Old English and French Masters
	Trumpet Tune II	GS	Introduction to Piano Classics, Vol. I (Mirovitch)
RAMEAU, J. P. (1683-1764)	Le Lardon	BH	Airs and Dances, Bk. II (Dorolle)
	Minuet in C	He	A Little Treasury of Classics, Bk. I (Lambert)
	Minuet en Rondeau	BH	Airs and Dances, Bk. I (Dorolle)
	Minuet in G Minor	U Su	Old Masters for Young Pianists (Kuranda) Recital Repertoire, Bk. I (Podolsky)
	Old French Dance	SG	Classics from the 17th and 18th Centuries
REICHARDT, J. F. (1752-1814)	Allegretto in A	Sch	Simple Short Piano Pieces
	Un poco presto e scherzando in D		
ROLLE, J. H. (1718-1785)	Minuet in B-flat	Sch	Simple Short Piano Pieces
RUDORF, C. F. (2nd half of 18th Century)	Polonaise in F	Sch	Clavierstücke für Anfänger

Composer	Title	Publisher	Volume or Collection
SCARLATTI, D. (1685-1757)	Allegro in G Minor	He	A Little Treasury of Classics, Bk. IV (Lambert)
	Giga in D Minor		
	Larghetto in D Minor		A Treasury of Easy Classics (Abrams)
SCHMIEDT, S. (1756-1799)	Vivace in G	Sch GS	Simple Short Piano Pieces Introduction to Piano Classics, Vol. II (Mirovitch)
STÖLZEL, G. (1690-1749)	Air italien	P	Contemporaries of Telemann
	Bourrée in G Minor		
TELEMANN, G. P. (1681-1767)	Gigue à l'Angloise	K	The Direct Path (Herrmann)
	Loure in A Minor	P	Contemporaries of Telemann
	Menuett (From A Minor Suite)		
TÜRK, D. G. (TUERK) (1750-1813)	Climbing	He	A Little Treasury of Classics, Bk. III (Lambert)
	Kleine Sonate Allegro ma non tanto Larghetto con tenerezza Poco allegro	Sch	Clavier Sonatinen (Kreutz)
	The Gazelle	CF	Road to Piano Artistry, Vol. II (Scionti)
	Twenty Six Selected Pieces 23. Sadness 24. Climbing 25. Consonants 26. Carefree 27. Mourning 28. Sing and Swing 29. The Master 30. Happy Memory 31. Stately Dance 32. Worry 33. Sicilienne 34. The Actor 35. Trio 36. Chorale 37. Etude 38. Variation 39. The Drama 40. Twirling 41. Trumpets 42. Bad Temper 43. Variety 44. Violin and Piano 45. Canon 46. Grave 47. Left Hand Study 49. Fifth Finger	K	Türk: Forty-nine Pieces for Beginners
UHDE, J. O. (1725-1766)	Tempo di Minuetto in C	Sch	Clavierstücke für Anfänger

Composer	Title	Publisher	Volume or Collection
VANHALL, J. B. (1739-1813)	Aria in B-flat (Cantabile in B-flat)	GS	Introduction to Piano Classics, Vol. II (Mirovitch)
		Sch	Simple Short Piano Pieces
	Minuetto in G	GS	Introduction to Piano Classics, Vol. II (Mirovitch)
		Sch	Simple Short Piano Pieces
WAGENSEIL, G. (1715-1777)	Allegro in F	U	Grosse Meister für kleine Hände
	Minuet in F	SG	Classics of the Seventeenth and Eighteenth Centuries (Tapper)
WITTHAUER, J. G. (1750-1802)	Allegro scherzando in G	Sch	Clavierstücke für Anfänger
	Polonaise in D		
	Poco vivace in A		
YOUNG, A. (18th Century)	Sarabande	BH	Early English Keyboard Music (Rowley)

MUSIC OF THE NINETEENTH CENTURY

Composer	Title	Publisher	Volume or Collection
BEETHOVEN, L. van (1770–1827)	Allemande in A	Sch P	Kleine Tänze (Frey) (No. 5) Ecossaisen und Deutsche Tanze (No. 8)
	Allemande in E-flat	Sch P	Kleine Tänze (Frey) (No. 9) Ecossaisen und Deutsche Tanze (No. 5)
	Allemande in G	Sch P	Kleine Tänze (Frey) (No. 14) Ecossaisen und Deutsche Tanze (No. 6)
	Country Dance in D	Sch H	Kleine Tänze (Frey) (No. 3) Easiest Original Pieces (No. 2)
	Country Dance in D	Sch GS	Kleine Tänze (Frey) (No. 11) Seven Landrische Tänze (No. 1)
	(Country Dance I)	GS	Master Series for the Young
	(Country Dance I)	CF	Road to Piano Artistry, Vol. I (Scionti)
	Country Dance in D Minor	Sch	Kleine Tänze (Frey) (No. 6)
	Country Dance in D Minor	H	Easiest Original Pieces (No. 3)
	Für Elise	GS GS GS B	Published Separately Master Series for the Young Thirty-two Sonatinas and Rondos Hours with the Masters, Bk. III
	German Dances (Complete)	K	Six German Dances by Ludwig van Beethoven
	German Dance in A	P	Ecossaises und Deutsche Tänze (No. 2)
	German Dance in B-flat		(No. 4)
	German Dance in C		(No. 1)
	German Dance in C		(No. 7)
	German Dance in F		(No. 3)
	German Dance in G		(No. 6)
	German Dance in G	He	A Little Treasury of Classics, Bk. I (Lambert)
	Gertrude's Dream Waltz	GS	Published Separately
	Ländrer in E-flat	Sch	Kleine Tänze (Frey) (No. 18)
	Menuett in A		(No. 20)
	Menuett in B-flat		(No. 16)
	Menuett in B-flat (Minuet II)	H	(No. 13) Easiest Original Classics
	Menuett in E-flat	Sch	Kleine Tänze (Frey) (No. 10)
	Menuett in E-flat		(No. 17)
	Menuett in E-flat	GS Su	Master Series for the Young Recital Repertoire, Bk. I (Podolsky)

Composer	Title	Publisher	Volume or Collection
BEETHOVEN, L. van (cont.)	Menuett in G	Sch	Kleine Tänze (Frey) (No. 4)
		H	Easiest Original Pieces
		GS	Master Series for the Young
	Sonatina in F	P	Sonatinen Vorstufe
	Allegro assai	P	Beethoven Sonatinas
	Rondo	K	
		Wo	Sonatina Album, Bk. II
		CF	Road to Piano Artistry, Vol. III (Scionti)
	Sonatina in G	P	Sonatinen Vorstufe
	Moderato	P	Beethoven Sonatinas
	Romanza	K	
		PP	Hundred Best Short Classics, Bk. I
		CF	Road to Piano Artistry, Vol. I (Scionti)
	Viennese Waltz in B-flat	Sch	Kleine Tänze (Frey) (No. 8)
	Viennese Waltz in D		(No. 19)
	Viennese Waltz in E-flat		(No. 15)
BERTINI, D. (1798-1876)	Andante in G (From Petits Morceaux)	P	Sonatinen Vorstufe (No. 4)
BURGMÜLLER, N. (1810-1836)	Confidence	CF	Road to Piano Artistry, Vol. II (Scionti)
	L'Adieu (The Farewell)	GS	Twenty-five Easy and Progressive Studies, Op. 100
	La Chevaleresque (Spirit of Chivalry)	GS	Twenty-five Easy and Progressive Studies, Op. 100
	La Pastorale	GS	Twenty-five Easy and Progressive Studies, Op. 100
		CF	Road to Piano Artistry, Vol. I (Scionti)
	La petite reunion (The Little Party)	GS	Twenty-five Easy and Progressive Studies, Op. 100
	La Styrienne		
	Le Retour (The Return)		
CHOPIN, F. (1810-1849)	Prelude in A, Op. 28	K	Chopin Preludes, Op. 28 (No. 7)
		GS	
		GS	Master Series for the Young
		H	Easiest Original Pieces
		PP	Hundred Best Short Classics, Bk. IV
	Prelude in C Minor, Op. 28	GS	Chopin Preludes, Op. 28, (No. 20)
		K	
		GS	Master Series for the Young
		H	Easiest Original Pieces
		PP	Hundred Best Short Classics, Bk. IV
CLEMENTI, M. (1752-1832)	Air Suisse, From Sonatina, Op. 36, No. 5	GS	Six Sonatinas, Op. 36, Clementi
		GS	Album of Sonatinas
		P	
		GS	Thirty-two Sonatinas and Rondos
	Andante con espressione, From Sonatina Op. 36, No. 4	GS	Six Sonatinas, Op. 36: Clementi
		GS	Album of Sonatinas
		P	

Composer	Title	Publisher	Volume or Collection
CLEMENTI, M. (cont.)		GS	Thirty-two Sonatinas and Rondos
		Be	Hours with the Masters, Bk. I
		CF	Road to Piano Artistry, Vol. V (Scionti)
	Sonatina in C, Op. 36, No. 1		Six Sonatinas, Op. 36: Clementi
	Spiritoso	GS	Thirty-two Sonatinas and Rondos
	Andante	P	Album of Sonatinas
	Vivace	GS	
	Sonatina in G, Op. 36, No. 2	GS	Six Sonatinas, Op. 36: Clementi
	Allegretto	P	Album of Sonatinas
	Allegretto	GS	
	Allegro	GS	Thirty-two Sonatinas and Rondos
	Sonatina in F, Op. 38, No. 3	GS	Selected Sonatinas, Bk. I
	Allegro		
	Allegretto		
	Waltz in G	P	Sonatinen Vorstufe (Preparatory Sonatina Album)
GADE, N. (1817-1890)	Boy's Merry-Go-Round, Op. 36, No. 4	GS	Selected Piano Solos by Romantic Composers, Bk. I
	The Children's Christmas Eve	GS	The Children's Christmas Eve, Op. 36
	1. The Christmas Bells		
	2. Christmas Song		
	3. The Christmas Tree		
	4. Boy's Merry-Go-Round		
	5. Dance of Little Girls		
	6. Good Night		
GRIEG, E. (1843-1907)	Albumleaf, Op. 12, No. 7	P	Lyrical Pieces, Op. 12
		GS	
		GS	Grieg: Forty-five Selected Compositions, Bk. I
		GS	Master Series for the Young
		He	A Little Treasury of Classics, Bk. IV (Lambert)
	Arietta, Op. 12, No. 1	P	Lyrical Pieces, Op. 12
		GS	
	Grandmother's Minuet, Op. 68, #2	P	Lyrical Pieces, Op. 68
		GS	
		GS	Grieg: Forty-five Selected Compositions, Bk. I
		GS	Master Series for the Young
	Patriotic Song, Op. 12, No. 8	P	Lyrical Pieces, Op. 12
		GS	
		GS	Master Series for the Young
	Walzer, Op. 12, No. 2	P	Lyrical Pieces, Op. 12
		GS	
		GS	Master Series for the Young
		GS	Grieg: Forty-five Selected Compositions, Bk. I
		He	A Treasury of Easy Classics (Abrams)
		P	Sonatinen Vorstufe (Preparatory Sonatina Album)

Composer	Title	Publisher	Volume or Collection
GRIEG, E. (cont.)	Watchman's Song, Op. 12 No. 3	P GS	Lyrical Pieces, Op. 12
		GS	Grieg: Forty-five Selected Compositions, Bk. I
		GS	Master Series for the Young
GURLITT, C. (1820–1901)	Album Leaves 2. Morning Prayer 14. Valse Noble 15. Loss	GS	Album Leaves for the Young, Op. 101
	Buds and Blossoms, Op. 107, No. 1	GS	Selected Piano Solos by Romantic Composers, Bk. II
	Impromptu, Op. 224, No. 5	B	Hours with the Masters, Bk. II
	In The Church, Op. 140, No. 12	GS	Selected Compositions by Romantic Composers, Bk. I
	Ländler, Op. 130, No. 8		
	Melodious Studies 4. March Violets 7. Old and Young 8. Pleasures of the Chase 9. A New Start 10. Patriotic Song 11. March 21. Dance of the Elves 23. Impatience	GS	Twenty-four Melodious Studies, Op. 131
	Minuet, Op. 224, No. 4	B	Hours with the Masters, Bk. II
HELLER, S. (1813–1888)	Selections from Op. 45 1. The Brook 5. The Maypole 7. Determination 8. Barcarolle 9. Heavenly Voices 10. Evening Prayer 14. Sailor's Song 16. Il Penseroso 18. Impatience	R GS	Twenty-five Studies for Piano, Op. 45
	Selections from Op. 46 2. Village Bells 3. In a Canoe 6. Gentle Caresses 7. Tarantelle 11. Moonbeams on the River 22. The Court Dance	R GS	Thirty Studies for Piano, Op. 46
	Selections from Op. 47 1. Helter Skelter 2. The Babbling Brook 4. Pleasant Thoughts 5. On the Alert 6. The Windmill 7. The Horse Race 9. The Sailboat	R GS	Twenty-five Studies for Piano, Op. 47

Composer	Title	Publisher	Volume or Collection
HELLER, S. (cont.)	10. Sounds of the Valley		
	11. Pastoral		
	12. Imps at Play		
	13. The Coach		
	14. Barcarolle		
	15. Claire de Lune		
	16. Joyous Meeting		
	17. Butterflies		
	19. A Memento		
	21. Romance		
	23. Story Told at Twilight		
	A Memento, Op. 47, No. 19	GS	Fifty Selected Studies: Heller (No. 3)
	(Berceuse)	PP	Hundred Best Short Classics, Bk. I
	Butterflies, Op. 47, No. 17	GS	Fifty Selected Studies: Heller (No. 4)
	Celestial Voices, Op. 45, No. 9	GS	Selected Piano Solos by Romantic Composers, Bk. I
		GS	Fifty Selected Studies: Heller (No. 21)
	Curious Story, Op. 138, No. 9	GS	Published Separately
		CF	Road to Piano Artistry, Vol. III (Scionti)
	Determination, Op. 45, No. 7	GS	Fifty Selected Studies: Heller (No. 18)
		GS	Selected Piano Solos by Romantic Composers, Bk. II
	Etude, Op. 45, No. 1	H	Contemporaries of Schumann
	(Etude in C)	B	Hours with the Masters, Bk. III
		GS	Fifty Selected Studies: Heller (No. 15)
	Etude in B Minor	CF	Road to Piano Artistry, Vol. III (Scionti)
	Evening Prayer, Op. 45, No. 10	GS	Fifty Selected Studies: Heller (No. 22)
	Gentle Caresses, Op. 46, No. 6		(No. 34)
	Gypsies I	CF	Road to Piano Artistry, Vol. II (Scionti)
	Il Penseroso, Op. 45, No. 16	GS	Published Separately
		GS	Fifty Selected Studies: Heller (No. 25)
	Impatience, Op. 45, No. 18	GS	Published Separately
		GS	Fifty Selected Studies: Heller (No. 26)
	In a Canoe, Op. 46, No. 3		Fifty Selected Studies: Heller (No. 32)
	In the Highlands of Scotland (Pastorale), Op. 47, No. 11	He	A Little Treasury of Classics, Bk. II (Lambert)
	Little Caprice	CF	Road to Piano Artistry, Vol. II (Scionti)
	Little Etude, Op. 47, No. 1	CF	Road to Piano Artistry, Vol. I (Scionti)
	Moonbeams on the River Op. 46, No. 11	GS	Fifty Selected Studies: Heller (No. 38)
	On the Alert, Op. 47, No. 5		(No. 6)
	Sailor's Song, Op. 45, No. 14	GS	Published Separately
		GS	Fifty Selected Studies: Heller (No. 23)
			Selected Piano Solos by Romantic Composers, Bk. II

Composer	Title	Publisher	Volume or Collection
HELLER, S. (cont.)	Study in E, Op. 47, No. 16	GS	Selected Piano Solos by Romantic Composers, Bk. II
		GS	Fifty Selected Studies: Heller (No. 13)
	Study in G, Op. 47, No. 4 (Pleasant Thoughts)	GS	Selected Piano Solos by Romantic Composers, Bk. I
		GS	Fifty Selected Studies: Heller (No. 5)
	Sounds of the Valley, Op. 47, No. 10	GS	Fifty Selected Studies: Heller (No. 8)
	Story at Twilight, Op. 47, No. 23		(No. 12)
	Tarantelle, Op. 46, No. 7		(No. 35)
		CF	Road to Piano Artistry, Vol. IV (Scionti)
		PP	Hundred Best Short Classics, Bk. II
		He	A Treasury of Easy Classics (Abrams)
	(Etude in E Minor)	B	Hours with the Masters, Bk. III
	(Petite Tarantelle)	GS	Published Separately
	The Babbling Brook, Op. 47, No. 2	GS	Fifty Selected Studies: Heller (No. 1)
	The Coach, Op. 47, No. 13		(No. 10)
	The Maypole, Op. 45, No. 5		(No. 20)
	The Sailboat, Op. 47, No. 9		(No. 7)
	The Windmill, Op. 47, No. 6		(No. 9)
KUHLAU, F. (1786-1832)	Sonatina in C, Op. 55, No. 1	P	Album of Sonatinas
	Allegro	GS	
	Cantabile	GS	Kuhlau Sonatinas, Bk. I
		GS	Thirty-two Sonatinas and Rondos
		He	Little Treasury of Sonatinas, Bk. II
	Sonatina in G, Op. 55, No. 2	P	Album of Sonatinas
	Allegretto	GS	
	Cantabile	GS	Kuhlau Sonatinas, Bk. I
	Allegro	GS	Thirty-two Sonatinas and Rondos
			Road to Piano Artistry, Vol. IV (Scionti)
KULLAK, T. (1818-1882)	Boating on the Lake (Barcarolle), Op. 62, No. 7		Road to Piano Artistry, Vol. I (Scionti)
	Scenes From Childhood, Op. 62	GS	Scenes From Childhood
	1. Once Upon A Time		
	2. The Clock		
	3. Sunday Morning		
	4. On The Playground		
	5. Little Cradle Song		
	6. Dance On The Lawn		
	7. Barcarolle		
	8. Grand Parade		
	9. The Birdie's Death		
	10. The Mill By The Brook		
	11. Skating		
	12. Evening Bell		

Composer	Title	Publisher	Volume or Collection
KULLAK, T. (cont.)	Scenes From Childhood, Op. 81	GS	Scenes From Childhood
	1. Child's Prayer		
	2. The Little Wanderer		
	3. Grandmother Tells A Ghost Story		
	4. Opening of the Children's Party		
	5. Loving Soul and Pure Heart Gay		
	6. The Race		
	7. The Angels in the Dream		
	8. The Nightingale		
	9. Spinning-Song		
	10. The Ghost in the Fireplace		
	11. The Little Hunters		
	12. The Little Rope-Dancer		
	The Clock, Op. 62, No. 2	CF	Road to Piano Artistry, Vol. VI (Scionti)
		GS	Selected Compositions by Romantic Composers, Bk. I
	The Ghost in the Fireplace, Op. 81, No. 10		Selected Compositions by Romantic Composers, Bk. I
	The Mill By The Brook, Op. 62, No. 10	CF	Road to Piano Artistry, Vol. V
	The Nightingale, Op. 81, No. 8	GS	Selected Compositions by Romantic Composers, Bk. I
		CF	Road to Piano Artistry, Vol. II (Scionti)
	The Race, Op. 81, No. 6		Selected Compositions by Romantic Composers, Bk. I
LIADOV, A. (1855-1914)	Four Russian Folk Songs	L	Four Russian Folk Songs (Siloti)
	1. On The Steppes	L	The Student Pianist, Vol. I (Mirovitch)
	2. A Day At The Fair		
	3. Sleep, My Child		
	4. I Danced With A Mosquito		
MACDOWELL, E. (1861-1908)	An Old Garden, Op. 62, No. 1	AS	New England Idylls, Op. 62
	Forgotten Fairy Tales	AS	Forgotten Fairy Tales
	1. Sung Outside the Prince's Door		
	2. Of A Tailor and a Bear		
	3. From Dwarf-land		
	4. Beauty in the Rosegarden		
	Song, Op. 55, No. 5	AS	Sea Pieces, Op. 55
	To A Wild Rose, Op. 51, No. 1	AS	Woodland Sketches, Op. 51
SCHUBERT, F. (1797-1828)	Ecossaises, Op. 33	P	Schubert Dances
		GS	

Composer	Title	Publisher	Volume or Collection
SCHUBERT, F. (cont.)		A	Beringer's School of Easy Classics: Schubert
		H	Easiest Original Pieces
		B	Hours With the Masters, Bk. III
	Ecossaise in D, No. 5 (From Five Ecossaises)	A	Beringer's School of Easy Classics: Schubert
		Su	Recital Repertoire, Bk. II (Podolsky)
SCHUMANN, R. (1810-1856)	First Loss, Op. 68, No. 16	P	Album for the Young, Op. 68
		GS	
		GS	Master Series for the Young
		He	A Treasury of Easy Classics (Abrams)
	Folk Song, Op. 68, No. 9	P	Album for the Young, Op. 68
		GS	
		GS	Selected Piano Solos by Romantic Composers, Bk. II
		A	Beringer's School of Easy Classics: Schumann
	Harvest Song, Op. 68, No. 24	P	Album for the Young, Op. 68
		GS	
	Hunting Song, Op. 68, No. 24	P	
		GS	
		GS	Master Series for the Young
		B	Hours with the Masters, Bk. II
		He	A Little Treasury of Classics, Bk. IV (Lambert)
	Knight Rupert, Op. 68, No. 12	P	Album for the Young, Op. 68
		GS	
		GS	Selected Piano Solos by Romantic Composers, Bk. I
		A	Beringer's School of Easy Classics: Schumann
		CF	Road to Piano Artistry, Vol. IV (Scionti)
	Little Romance, Op. 68, No. 19	P	Album for the Young, Op. 68
		GS	
		GS	Master Series for the Young
	Little Study, Op. 68, No. 14	P	Album for the Young, Op. 68
		GS	
		GS	Master Series for the Young
		GS	Selected Piano Solos by Romantic Composers, Bk. I
	Poor Orphan, Op. 68, No. 6	P	Album for the Young, Op. 68
		GS	
		A	Beringer's School of Easy Classics: Schumann
		B	Hours with the Masters, Bk. II
		PP	Hundred Best Short Classics, Bk. I
		GS	Selected Piano Solos by Romantic Composers, Bk. II
	Reaper's Song, Op. 68, No. 18	P	Album for the Young, Op. 68
		GS	
		A	Beringer's School of Easy Classics: Schumann

Composer	Title	Publisher	Volume or Collection
SCHUMANN, R. (cont.)		B	Hours with the Masters, Bk. II
		GS	Master Series for the Young
		CF	Road to Piano Artistry, Vol. II (Scionti)
		P	Sonatinen Vorstufe
	Rustic Song, Op. 68, No. 20	P	Album for the Young, Op. 68
		GS	
		B	Hours with the Masters, Bk. III
	Sicilienne, Op. 68, No. 11	P	Album for the Young, Op. 68
		GS	
		A	Beringer's School of Easy Classics: Schumann
		GS	Selected Piano Solos by Romantic Composers, Bk. I
	The Rider's Story, Op. 68, No. 23	P	Album for the Young, Op. 68
		GS	
		GS	Master Series for the Young
		GS	Selected Piano Solos by Romantic Composers, Bk. II
	The Wild Horseman, Op. 68, No. 8	P	Album for the Young, Op 68
		GS	
		A	Beringer's School of Easy Classics: Schumann
		He	A Little Treasury of Classics, Bk. III (Lambert)
		GS	Master Series for the Young
		He	A Treasury of Easy Classics (Abrams)
TSCHAIKOWSKY, P. (1840-1893)	At Church, Op. 39, No. 24	GS	Album for the Young, Op. 39
		GS	Master Series for the Young
	Farmer's Boy Playing on the Accordian, Op. 39, No. 12	GS	Album for the Young, Op. 39
		GS	Master Series for the Young
	Italian Song, Op. 39, No. 15	GS	Album for the Young, Op. 39
		GS	Master Series for the Young
	Mama, Op. 39, No. 4	GS	Album for the Young, Op. 39
	March of the Tin Soldiers, Op. 39, No. 5	GS	Album for the Young, Op. 39
	Mazurka, Op. 39, No. 10	GS	Album for the Young, Op. 39
		GS	Master Series for the Young
		PP	Hundred Best Short Classics, Bk. II
		CF	Road to Piano Artistry, Vol. II (Scionti)
	Morning Prayer, Op. 39, No. 1	GS	Album for the Young, Op. 39
		GS	Master Series for the Young
		He	A Little Treasury of Classics, Bk. III (Lambert)
		GS	Selected Piano Solos by Romantic Composers, Bk. I
	Russian Song, Op. 39, No. 11	GS	Album for the Young, Op. 39
		GS	Master Series for the Young
	Sweet Dreams, Op. 39, No. 21	GS	Album for the Young, Op. 39
		GS	Master Series for the Young

Composer	Title	Publisher	Volume or Collection
TSCHAIKOWSKY, P. (cont.)		H	Contemporaries of Schumann
		H	Easiest Original Classics
		CF	Road to Piano Artistry, Vol. II (Scionti)
		He	A Treasury of Easy Classics (Abrams)
	Song of the Lark, Op. 39, No. 22	GS	Album for the Young, Op. 39
		GS	Master Series for the Young
		CF	Road to Piano Artistry, Vol. VI (Scionti)
		GS	Selected Piano Solos by Romantic Composers, Bk. I
		GS	Published Separately
	The New Doll, Op. 39, No. 9	GS	Album for the Young, Op. 39
		GS	Master Series for the Young
		PP	Hundred Best Short Classics, Bk. I
	The Organgrinder, Op. 39, No. 23	GS	Album for the Young, Op. 39
		GS	Master Series for the Young
WEBER, C. (1786-1826)	Allemande in E-flat	Su	Recital Repertoire, Bk. I (Podolsky)
	German Waltz	He	Little Treasury of Classics, Bk. II
	Original Theme, Op. 9	GS	Master Series for the Young
	Waltz in G	He	A Little Treasury of Classics, Bk. III (Lambert)

MUSIC OF THE TWENTIETH CENTURY

Composer	Title	Publisher	Volume or Collection
ANTHEIL, GEORGE (1900-)	Suite for the Piano 1. Practice Hours Are Long 2. In Spain with Mr. Hemingway 3. Someday We'll Like Stravinsky	GS	Suite for the Piano
BADINGS, HENK (1907-)	Reihe kleiner Klavierstücke 1. Intrada 2. Siciliano 3. Ballo Gaio 4. Air 5. Rondo popolare 6. Menuet 7. Scherzo Pastorale 8. Rondo-Finale	Sch	Reihe kleiner Klavierstücke
BARTÓK, BÉLA (1881-1945)	Dance Tune	MMC BH L K	Meet Modern Music, Pt. II For Children, Vol. I (No. 12) 42 Hungarian Folk Melodies (No. 12) Little Pieces for Children, Vol. I (No. 12)
	Energy	MMC BH L K	Meet Modern Music, Pt. II For Children, Vol. I (No. 21) 42 Hungarian Folk Melodies (No. 21) Little Pieces for Children, Vol. I (No. 21)
	From "For Children," Vol. I, Numbers 12, 21, 23, 26, 28, 32, 33, 35-40	BH	For Children, Vol. I
	From "For Children," Vol. II, Numbers 11, 18, 21, 22, 25, 26, 27, 29, 33, 34, 36, 37, 39, 40	BH	For Children, Vol. II
	From "Hungarian Folk Melodies", Numbers 12, 21, 23, 26, 28, 30, 31, 34, 35, 37-40	L	42 Hungarian Folk Melodies (Same contents as "For Children," Vol. I except nos. 25 and 31)
	From "Little Pieces for Children", Numbers 12 and 21	K	Little Pieces for Children, Vol. I (Same contents as Nos. 1-22 of "42 Hungarian Folk Melodies," and "For Children," Vol. I)
	From "Mikrokosmos," Vol. III Hungarian Dance Merriment Variations	BH	Mikrokosmos, Vol. III

Composer	Title	Publisher	Volume or Collection
BARTÓK, BÉLA (cont.)	From "Mikrokosmos," Vol. IV Melody in the Mist Nutturno	BH	Mikrokosmos, Vol. IV
	From "Piano Pieces for Children", Numbers 23, 26, 28, 30, 31, 34, 35, 37-42	K	Piano Pieces for Children, Vol. II (Same as nos. 23-42 of "42 Hungarian Folk Melodies")
	From "16 Pieces for Children", Numbers 9, 10, 11, 16	I	16 Pieces for Children (Contents selected from "For Children," Vol. I, and "Ten Easy Pieces")
	From "Ten Easy Pieces for Children" Dedication Flight Sostenuto Evening in the Country Hungarian Folksong Sunrise	K	Ten Easy Pieces for Children
BARVINSKY (1888-)	Lullaby	W	Modern Russian Piano Music
	Round Dance	L	Children's Piano Pieces by Soviet Composers
	Mr. and Mrs. Beetle	W	Modern Russian Piano Music
	The Mouse and the Bear	W L	Modern Russian Piano Music Children's Piano Pieces by Soviet Composers
	The Little Mosquito	L	Children's Piano Pieces by Soviet Composers
	The Little Rabbit		
	The Little Sparrow		
	Mr. Rooster Threshes Wheat		
	Round Dance		
BLOCH, ERNEST (1880-)	Ten Pieces for Children 1. Lullaby 2. The Joyous Party 3. With Mother 4. Elves 5. Joyous March 6. Melody 7. Pastorale 8. Rainy Day 9. Teasing 10. Dream	CF CF	Enfantines Published Separately
BORTKIEWICZ, S. (1877-)	Nine Easy Piano Pieces, Op. 54 1. Russian Peasant Girl 2. The Cossack 3. The Spanish Dancer	AMP	Marionettes, Op. 54

Composer	Title	Publisher	Volume or Collection
BORTKIEWICZ, S. (cont.)	4. The Tyrolese 5. The Gypsy 6. The Marchioness 7. The Chinaman 8. Teddy Bear 9. Harlequin		
BOWLES, PAUL (1910-)	Folk Preludes 3. Whar Did You Cum From 5. Cape Ann 6. Ole Tare River 7. Kentucky Moonshiner	MMC	Folk Preludes
BRIDGE, FRANK (1844-1924)	Miniature Pastorals (Set I) 1. Allegretto con moto 2. Tempo di Valse 3. Allegretto ben moderato	BH	Miniature Pastorals for Piano
CARVAJAL, ARMANDO (?)	Miniature	MMC	Meet Modern Music, Part II
	Tristess	MMC	Meet Modern Music, Part II
CASELLA, ALFREDO (1883-1947)	Children's Pieces 1. Preludio 6. Siciliano	AMP	Eleven Children's Pieces
CASTRO, JUAN JOSE (1895-)	Bear Dance	CF	Masters of Our Day
COPLAND, AARON (1900-)	Sunday Afternoon Music	CF	Masters of Our Day
COWELL, HENRY (1897-)	The Irishman Dances	CF	Masters of Our Day
CRESTON, PAUL (1906-)	Five Little Dances 1. Rustic Dance 2. Languid Dance 3. Toy Dance 4. Pastoral Dance 5. Festive Dance	GS	Five Little Dances, Op. 24
DELUNE, LOUIS (1876-)	Cinq Morceaux Faciles 1. Automobile 2. Gracieusement 3. A dos d'Ane 4. Le chevrier qui passe 5. La Senorita Conchita	E E	Cinq Morceaux Faciles Pour Piano Published Separately
DIAMOND, DAVID (1915-)	Album for the Young Little March Waltz Happy-Go-Lucky Tender Thoughts A Gambol Christmastide	EV	Album for the Young

Composer	Title	Publisher	Volume or Collection
DIAMOND, DAVID (cont.)	Spring Song The Sad Slant-Eyed Boy Jostling Joe The Day's End		
ELWELL, HERBERT (1898-)	Bus Ride	CF	Masters of our Day
	Tarantella		
FREED, ISADORE (1900-)	Jeneral Jerry's Jolly Jugglers	CF	Masters of our Day
	With Trumpets and Drums		

FULEIHAN, ANIS (1900-)	Set of Five
	  1. An Old-time Song
	  2. On the March
	  3. Casual Waltz
	  4. Conversation and Chorale
	  5. Eccentric Dance
		MMC	Set of Five

	Short Pieces
	  3. Sentimental Journey
	  4. Stealthy Tread
	  5. Brisk March
		So	Five Very Short Pieces for Talented Young Bipeds

GLIÉRE, REINHOLD (1875-1926)	In A Monastary	SG	Russian Piano Classics
GOEDICKE, ALEXANDER (1877-)	A Gay Prank	L	The Student Pianist, Vol. I (Mirovitch)
	Butterflies	SG	Russian Piano Classics
	Gavotte	SG	Russian Piano Classics
	In a Quiet Mood	MMC	Meet Modern Music, Pt. I
	Sadness	L	The Student Pianist, Vol. I (Mirovitch)
	Slow Waltz	L	Children's Piano Pieces by Soviet Composers
	The Blacksmith Works		
GOOSSENS, EUGENE (1893-)	Bonzo's Dance	CF	Masters of our Day
	Pikki's Lament		

GREEN, RAY (1909-)	Four Pieces for Piano Solo
	  1. Piece to Begin
	  2. March
	  3. Melody
	  4. Piece to End
		AME	Pieces for Children

GRETCHANINOFF, ALEXANDER (1864-)	Gouaches
	  1. At Joyful Work
	  2. In Solitude
	  3. Encounter
		L	Gouaches, Op. 189

	Holidays	MMC	Meet Modern Music, Pt. I
	Mommy		

Composers	Title	Publisher	Volume or Collection

GRETCHANINOFF, ALEXANDER (cont.)	Six Pieces from "Album de Nina"
	  2. Chansonnette
	  4. Songerie
	  5. Marche
	  6. Mélodie Antique
	  8. Au crépuscule
	  10. En Promenade
		E	Album de Nina, Op. 141

	Six Pieces from "A Child's Day"
	  5. Father and Mother
	  6. A Visit to Grandmother
	  7. Grandmother's Waltz
	  8. The Happy Return Home
	  9. Nurse's Tale
	  10. Bedtime
		Sch	A Child's Day, Op. 109

HALFFTER, RUDOLFO (1905-)	Danza de Avila	CF	Masters of our Day
HANSON, HOWARD (1896-)	Dance of the Warriors	CF	Masters of our Day
	Enchantment		
	The Bell		

HINDEMITH, PAUL (1895-)	Easy 5-Tone Pieces
	  1. Massig Schnell
	  2. Ruhig bewegt
	  3. Munter, Schnell Viertal
	  4. Lebhaft, sehr markiert
	  5. Schnell, Ganze Takte
	  6. Gemächlich
	  7. Schnell und Wild
	  8. Massig Schnell
	  9. Langsam, ruhig shreitend
	  10. Munter, zimlich lebhaft
	  11. Massig Schnell
	  12. Bewegt
		Sch	Kleine Klaviermusik (Sing-Und Spielmusiken, No. 4)

	Wir Bauen Eine Stadt
	  1. Marsch
	  2. Lied
	  3. Musikstück
	  4. Lied
	  5. Man spielt „Besuch"
	  6. Die Diebe kommen in der nacht
		Sch	Wir Bauen Eine Stadt

KABALEVSKY, DMITRI (1904-)	A Cozy Waltz, Op. 39, No. 23	L	The Student Pianist, Vol. I (Mirovitch)
	A Little Fairy Tale	L I	15 Pieces for Children, Op. 27 18 Pieces for Children, Op. 27
	A Sad Story	L	Children's Piano Pieces by Soviet Composers
	A Short Story	L	15 Pieces for Children, Op. 27
	Ballad	I	18 Pieces for Children, Op. 27

Composer	Title	Publisher	Volume or Collection
KABALEVSKY, DMITRI (cont.)	Carefree, Op. 39, No. 22	L	The Student Pianist, Vol. I
	Dance	L	15 Pieces for Children, Op. 27 (No. 15)
	Dancing On The Lawn	L	15 Pieces for Children, Op. 27
		I	18 Pieces for Children, Op. 27
	Etude	L	15 Pieces for Children, Op. 27
		I	18 Pieces for Children, Op. 27
	Fairy Tale	I	18 Pieces for Children, Op. 27
	Four Little Pieces, Op. 14	L	Four Little Pieces, Op. 14
	1. The Drummer	W	Modern Russian Piano Music
	2. A Brisk Game	W	Modern Russian Piano Music
	3. In the Gymnasium (The Game)		
	4. Soldiers March		
	Gay Journey	I	24 Little Pieces for Children, Op. 39
	Having Fun	L	15 Pieces for Children, Op. 27
		I	18 Pieces for Children, Op. 27
	Improvization	I	24 Little Pieces for Children, Op. 39
	Joking (A Little Joke)	I	18 Pieces for Children, Op. 27
		L	15 Pieces for Children, Op. 27
		L	Children Piano Pieces by Soviet Composers
	Novelette, Op. 27	L	15 Pieces for Children, Op. 27
	Novelette, Op. 39	I	24 Little Pieces for Children, Op. 39
	Old Dance	L	15 Pieces for Children, Op. 27
		I	18 Pieces for Children, Op. 27
		L	Children's Piano Pieces by Soviet Composers
	Rondino	I	18 Pieces for Children, Op. 27
	Scherzo	I	18 Pieces for Children, Op. 27
		L	15 Pieces for Children, Op. 27
		L	Children's Piano Pieces by Soviet Composers
	Slow Waltz	I	24 Little Pieces for Children, Op. 39
	Soldier's Dance	I	18 Pieces for Children, Op. 27
	Sonatina	I	18 Pieces for Children, Op. 27
		L	15 Pieces for Children, Op. 27
	The Clown, Op. 39, No. 20	L	The Student Pianist, Vol. I (Mirovitch)
	Toccatina	L	15 Pieces for Children, Op. 27
		I	18 Pieces for Children, Op. 27
	Waltz	I	18 Pieces for Children, Op. 27
KHACHATURIAN, ARAM (1903-)	Three Pieces from "Adventures of Ivan"	L	Adventures of Ivan (Mirovitch)
	1. Ivan Sings		
	2. Ivan Can't Go Out Today		
	3. Ivan Is Ill		

Composer	Title	Publisher	Volume or Collection

KODÁLY, ZOLTÁN (1882-)	From "Children's Dances"
	  4. Moderato cantabile
	  5. Allegro moderato, poco rubato
	  6. Vivace
	  7. Vivace quasi marcia
	  8. Friss
	  9. Allegro marcato
	  10. Allegretto leggiero
	  11. Vivace
	  12. Allegro comodo
		BH	Children's Dances

MAYKAPAR, SAMUEL (1867-)	At the Blacksmith's, Op. 8, No. 5 (The Blacksmith)	Su MMC	Recital Repertoire, Bk. II (Podolsky) Meet Modern Music, Pt. II
	Dewdrops	L	The Student Pianist, Vol. I (Mirovitch)
	Gavotte		
	Passing Fancy		
	The Little Shepherd		
	The Moth		
	The Music Box		

MENOTTI, GIAN-CARLO (1911-)	From "Poemetti"
	  2. Lullaby
	  3. Bells at Dawn
	  4. The Spinner
	  5. The Bagpipers
	  11. The Manger
		R	Poemetti

MIASKOWSKY, NIKOLAI (1881-1951)	A Small Duet	L	Children's Piano Pieces by Soviet Composers
	Harvest Song, Op. 14, No. 8	W	Modern Russian Piano Music
	In Old Fashioned Style	L	Children's Piano Pieces by Soviet Composers
	In Waltz Style		
	Spring Mood		

MILHAUD, DARIUS (1892-)	Three Pieces from "The Child Loves"
	  1. Flowers
	  2. Candy
	  3. Toys
		L	The Child Loves

PATTISON, LEE (1890-)	Columbine	Su	Published Separately
	Huntsman On The Hill		
	Marche Mignonne		
	Night Hymn at Sea		
	Tango		
	The Burro Ride		

Composer	Title	Publisher	Volume or Collection

PERSICHETTI, VINCENT (1915-)	Serenade, Op. 2, No. 2
	  1. Tune
	  2. Strum
	  3. Pluck
		EV	Serenade, Op. 2, No. 2

PINTO, OCTAVIO (1890-1950)	Children's Festival
	  1. Prelude
	  2. Menuet
	  3. Little March
	  4. Serenade
	  5. Playing Marbles
		GS	Children's Festival

PISK, PAUL (1893-)	From Old Mexicale	CF	Masters of our Day
POLDINI, EDWARD (1869-)	Dance of the Gnomes	GS	Published Separately
PROKOFIEFF, SERGE (1891-1953)	Evening, Op. 65, No. 11	L I L	Music for Children, Op. 65 (Summer Day Suite) Published Separately
	Fairy Tale, Op. 65, No. 3	L I L MMC	Music for Children, Op. 65 Published Separately Meet Modern Music, Pt. I
	March, Op. 65, No. 10	L I L W L	Music for Children, Op. 65 Published Separately Modern Russian Piano Music Children's Piano Pieces by Soviet Composers
	Moonlit Meadows, Op. 65, No. 12	L I	Music for Children, Op. 65
	Morning, Op. 65, No. 1		
	Parade of the Grasshopper, Op. 65, No. 7		
	Promenade, Op. 65, No. 2	L MMC W	Published Separately Meet Modern Music, Pt. I Modern Russian Piano Music
	Rain and the Rainbow, Op. 65, No. 8	L I	Music for Children, Op. 65
	Regrets, Op. 65, No. 5	L	Published Separately
	Tag, Op. 65, No. 9	L I	Music for Children, Op. 65
	Tarantella, Op. 65, No. 4		
	Waltz, Op. 65, No. 6	L L	Published Separately Children's Piano Pieces by Soviet Composers
RAKOFF, NICOLAS (1908-)	Valse	W	Modern Russian Piano Music

Composer	Title	Publisher	Volume or Collection
RATHAUS, KAROL (1895-)	Cross Talk	CF	Masters of our Day

REBIKOV, VLADIMIR
(1866-1920)
	Piano Album, No. I
	  1. Little Story
	  2. A Letter
	  3. Berceuse
	  4. Country Fair
	  5. Chinese Meditation
	  6. Chanson triste
	  7. Valse melancolique
	  8. Reverie
	  9. Mazurka
	 10. Tender Reproach
	 11. Turkish Dance
	 12. In pensive mood
	 13. In a mist
	 14. Elegie
	 15. Dance orientale
	 16. Dance caractérestique
		Sch	Piano Album, No. I (Rowley)

	Piano Album, No. II
	  1. In the Forest
	  2. Grotesque Dancer
	  6. Hope
	  8. Russian Doll
	  9. Lilies of the Valley
	 10. Valse Minature
	 11. Autumn Flowers
	 12. O Tell Me Why?
	 13. Movements Plastiques I
	 14. Movements Plastiques II
	 15. The Vast Abyss
	 17. Moments d'allegresse
	 18. Danse avec une Cloche
	 20. Pavane
	 21. Pages d'un manuscrit
	      oublié I
	 22. Pages d'un manuscrit
	      oublié II
		Sch	Piano Album, No. II (Rowley)

	Pictures for Children, Op. 37
	  1. A Little Girl Pleading
	     With Her Mother
	  2. Preparing the Lesson
	  3. A Picture from the
	     Ancient World
	  4. A Joyous Moment
	  5. Up On A Swing
	  6. Promenade of the
	     Gnomes
	  7. A Sad Story With A
	     Happy Ending
		I	Pictures for Children, Op. 37

	Silhouettes, Op. 31
	  Children Skating
	  Strolling Musicians
	  Playing Soldiers
		GS	Silhouettes, Op. 31

Composer	Title	Publisher	Volume or Collection
REBIKOV, VLADIMIR (cont.)	Evening in the Meadow Little Girl Rocking Her Dolly Shepherd Playing On His Pipe The Lame Witch Lurking in the Forest		
	Three Pieces from "Silhouettes," Op. 31 Children Skating Hurdy Gurdy (Strolling Musicians) Playing Soldiers	MMC	Meet Modern Music, Pt. I
REGER, MAX (1873-1916)	Jugend-Album I 1. Hasche mich! 2. Uber Stock und Stein 3. Frühlingsluft 4. Reigen 5. Ein Tänzchen 6. Frohsinn 7. Das Tote Vöglein	Sch	Jugend Album I
RHENE-BATON (1879-1940)	Musette Petit Choral	E E	Album Rose Published Separately
ROBB, J. D. (1892-)	Horseback Over The Sagebrush Plain, (From "Pictures of New Mexico")	AMP	Published Separately
ROZSA, MIKLOS (1907-)	Musette, From "Kaleidoscope," Op. 19	AMP	Published Separately
RUBINSTEIN, BERYL (1898-1953)	Homeward Bound The Brook	CF	A Day In The Country
	Musical Fancies, Series II 1. The Shepherd Boy 2. Minuet à la Reine 3. The Procession 4. Siciliana 5. The Little Match Girl	CF	Published Separately
SAMINSKY, LAZARE (1882-)	Firebell, Op. 45, No. 2 Parade, Op. 45, No. 4 Shadows, Op. 45, No. 3	CF	Masters of our Day
SCHMITT, FLORENT (1870-)	Entrée from "Petite Musiques," Op. 32	S	Les Chefs-D'Oeuvre des Grands Maitre Contemporains
SCHULTHESS, WALTER (1894-)	Glockenspiel	Sch	The New Piano Book, Vol. I

Composer	Title	Publisher	Volume or Collection
SCOTT, CYRIL (1879-)	A Little Dancer From Spain	Sch Sch	Miniatures Published Separately
	Solitude, from ''Young Hearts''	Sch	The New Piano Book, Vol. I
	Sunday Morn		
	The Zoo	Sch	The Zoo
	1. The Elephant		
	2. The Squirrel		
	3. The Bear		
	4. The Monkey		
	5. The Snake		
	6. The Giraffe		
	7. The Tortoise		
	8. The Rhinoceros		
SHULGIN, LEO	Children's Pieces	L	Ten Children's Pieces
	1. On the Steppes		
	2. On A Bicycle		
	3. In The Evening		
	4. Story		
	5. Cradle Song		
	6. Pioneer Meeting		
	7. Grandmother's Story		
	8. Turkmenian Song		
	9. Meditation		
	10. To the Sound of the Accordian		
SIBELIUS, JEAN (1865-)	Valsette	MMC	Meet Modern Music, Pt. I
SIEGMEISTER, ELIE (1909-)	From ''The Children's Day'' 1. Sunny Morning 2. Skipping Rope	L	The Children's Day
SLAVENSKI, JOSIP (1865-1930)	Albanian Song	Sch	The New Piano Book, Vol. I
STRAVINSKY, IGOR (1882-)	From ''The Five Fingers'' Allegro Heavily (Pesante)	O Sch MMC	The Five Fingers The New Piano Book, Vol. I Meet Modern Music, Pt. II
TANSMAN, ALEXANDRE (1897-)	From ''Children At Play''	L	Children at Play
	2. Two Voices		
	3. Elegy		
	4. Meditation		
	5. Game		
	6. Barcarolle		
	7. Song		
	8. Lullaby		
	9. Toccata		
	10. Poem		
	11. Peasant Dance		
	12. Invention		
	13. South American Dance		

Composer	Title	Publisher	Volume or Collection
TANSMAN, ALEXANDRE (cont.)	From ''Ten Diversions for the Young Pianist'' 1. Spanish Mood 2. Dreams 3. Merry-Go-Round 4. Melancholy 5. Rainy Day 6. Speeding Along 7. Calm 8. Prayer 9. Mischief	AMP	Ten Diversions for the Young Pianist
	Lullaby (From Children At Play)	L	Published Separately
	Piano Miniatures 1. Minuet 2. Caprice 3. Bourrée 4. Spleen	De	Piano Miniatures
	Pour les Enfants - Set I 1. Old Song 2. The Doll 3. The Bouncing Ball 4. The Dancing Bear 6. Russian Dance 9. Skating 11. Dream	AMP	Pour les Enfants Published Separately
	Set II 5. Meditation 7. The Spinning Top 8. The Young Swing Pianist 9. The Dancing Lesson 10. Arabian Nights 11. Mickey and Minnie 12. Parade		Published Separately
	Set III 1. Awakening 2. The Warbler 3. Noel 4. Petite Rêverie 5. Tin Soldiers 6. Rest 7. Coquette 8. The Scooter 9. A Difficult Problem 10. The Old Beggar 11. The Music Box 12. Ping-Pong		 Published Separately Published Separately Published Separately Published Separately Published Separately
	Set IV 1. An Old Tale 2. Rocking Horse 3. A Serious Moment 5. In A Venetian Gondola 6. Blues Record 7. Valse Lento 9. Berceuse		 Published Separately Published Separately

Composer	Title	Publisher	Volume or Collection
TCHÉREPNINE, ALEXANDRE (1899-)	Les Cloches tristes	D	Pour petits et grands - Set I
THOMPSON, RANDALL (1899-)	Little Prelude Song After Sundown	CF	Masters of our Day
THOMSON, VIRGIL (1896-)	A Day Dream Eccentric Dance	CF	Masters of Our Day

TOCH, ERNST (1887-)	From ''Echoes of A Small Town''
	  1. Little Kitten
	  2. Now I Lay Me Down To Sleep
	  6. Single File
	  13. Autumn Is Coming
		AMP	Echoes of A Small Town, Op. 49

	Gray Skies, Op. 40, No. 13 Sunbeams, Op. 20, No. 14	Sch	The New Piano Book, Vol. I

VILLA-LOBOS, HEITOR (1887-)	Francette et Piá
	  1. Piá Came to France
	  2. Piá Saw Francette
	  3. Piá Spoke to Francette
	  4. Piá and Francette Play Together
	  5. Francette Is Sorry
		E	Published Separately

WAXMAN, FRANZ (1906-)	From ''The Charm Bracelet''
	  1. Two Little Shoes
	  2. The Four Leaf Clover
		L	The Charm Bracelet

SECTION III

INTERMEDIATE

GRADES V AND VI

MUSIC OF THE SIXTEENTH, SEVENTEENTH
AND EIGHTEENTH CENTURIES

Composer	Title	Publisher	Volume or Collection
AGINCOURT, F. de (1684-1757)	L'Etourdie	BH	Airs and Dances, Bk. II (Dorolle)
ARNE, T. (1710-1778)	Gigue (From Sonata VI in G Minor)	SG	Classics of the 17th and 18th Centuries
		CF	Classic Sonatas (Podolsky)
		A	Beringer's School of Easy Classics: Old English and French Masters
		B	Hours with the Masters, Bk. III
		PP	Hundred Best Short Classics, Bk. I
	Minuet with Variations	A	Beringer's School of Easy Classics: Old English and French Masters
		SG	Classics of the 17th and 18th Centuries
		B	Hours with the Masters, Bk. III
		PP	Hundred Best Short Classics, Bk. I
	Sonata in B-flat	BH	Airs and Dances, Bk. I (Dorolle)
	Sonata in G Minor Affetuoso Gigue	CF	Classic Sonatas (Podolsky)
BACH, C.P.E. (1714-1788)	Alla Polacca, in A Minor	Sch	Die Söhne Bach
	Allegretto (From Sonata in F)	B	Hours with the Masters, Bk. II
	Andante in D	U	Old Masters for Young Pianists (Kuranda)
	Gigue in E Minor	He	Little Treasury of Classics, Bk. IV
	La Philippine	H	The Sons of Johann Sebastian Bach
	Minuet in E	C	Eighteenth Century Music, Vol. II
	Presto in B-flat		
	Rondo in E-flat	P	Sonatas and Pieces
	Sonata I in C Allegro tranquillamente Andante Tempo di Minuetto	Sch	Six Sonatas by C.P.E. Bach, Vol. I
BACH, J. C (1735-1782)	Allegretto (From Sonata Op. 5, No. 1)	EV	New Recital Repertoire (Mirovitch)
	Minuet (From Sonata in D, Op. 5, No. 2)	H	The Sons of Johann Sebastian Bach
	Tempo di Minuetto (From Sonata, Op. 5, No. 1)	EV	New Recital Repertoire (Mirovitch)

Composer	Title	Publisher	Volume or Collection
BACH, J. S. (1685-1750)	Allemande in A Minor	BMC CF	Bach for Early Grades, Bk, II Road to Piano Artistry, Vol. IV (Scionti)
	Aria für Klavier, in G Major	Sch K	Little Bach Book (No. 13) Little Notebook of Anna Magdalena Bach (pg. 77)
	Chorale "O, Ewigkeit du Donnerwort"		(pg. 121)
	Choral "Wer nurden lieben Gott lässt walten"		(pg. 55)
	Entrée in F	Sch	Little Bach Book (No. 2)
	Fughetta in B-flat	K	Various Short Preludes and Fugues (pg. 22)
	Fugue in C	 GS GS Sch	(pg. 24) Eighteen Little Preludes and Fugues (No. 15) Short Preludes and Fugues (pg. 22) Little Bach Book (No. 16)
	Gavotte in D (Gavotte II from English Suite VI in D Minor)	K P GS CF GS GS	English Suites Bach First Lessons, Bk. II (Carroll) First Lessons in Bach, Bk. II (Carroll) Bach Album (Heinze)
	Gavotte in G (From French suite V in G)	K P GS CF GS BMC GS B	French Suites Bach First Lessons, Bk. II (Carroll) First Lessons in Bach, Bk. II (Carroll) Bach for Early Grades, Bk. III Bach Album (Heinze) (pg. 4) Hours with the Masters, Bk. IV
	Gavotte in G Minor (From English Suite III)	K P GS GS GS CF MM	English Suites Master Series for the Young Bach Album (Heinze) Road to Piano Artistry, Vol. VI (Scionti) Your Bach Book (Maier)
	Gigue in C Minor (From French Suite II)	K P GS BMC	French Suites Bach for Early Grades, Bk. III
	Invention in A Minor	K P GS	Two-Part Inventions (No. 13)
	Invention in C	K	Two-Part Inventions (No. 1)

Composer	Title	Publisher	Volume or Collection
BACH, J. S. (Cont.)		P	
		GS	
		CF	Road to Piano Artistry, Vol. VII (Scionti)
	Invention in D Minor	K	Two-Part Inventions (No. 4)
		P	
		GS	
		MM	Your Bach Book (Maier)
		B	Hours with the Masters, Bk. IV
	Invention in E Minor	K	Two-Part Inventions (No. 7)
		P	
		GS	
	Invention in F	K	Two-Part Inventions (No. 8)
		P	
		GS	
		BMC	Bach for Early Grades, Bk. III
		PP	Hundred Best Short Classics, Bk. III
	Invention in F Minor	K	Two-Part Inventions (No. 9)
		P	
		GS	
	Little Prelude in C	K	Various Short Preludes and Fugues (pg. 16)
		P	Short Preludes and Fugues (pg. 17)
		GS	Short Preludes and Fugues (pg. 14)
		GS	Eighteen Little Preludes and Fugues (Key of B-flat) (No. 5)
		GS	Master Series for the Young (pg. 25)
	Little Prelude in C Minor	K	Various Short Preludes and Fugues (pg. 17)
		GS	Short Preludes and Fugues (pg. 15)
		P	Short Preludes and Fugues (pg. 18)
		Sch	Little Bach Book (No. 12)
		GS	Master Series for the Young
	Little Prelude in D Minor	K	Various Short Preludes and Fugues (pg. 9)
		GS	Short Preludes and Fugues (pg. 7)
		P	Short Preludes and Fugues (pg. 8)
		GS	Eighteen Little Preludes and Fugues (No. 2)
		BMC	Bach for Early Grades, Bk. II
		K	First Bach Book (No. 30)
		CF	Road to Piano Artistry, Vol. III (Scionti)
		Sch	Little Piano Book of Wilhelm Friedemann Bach (pg. 12)
	Little Prelude in D Minor	K	Various Short Preludes and Fugues (pg. 12)
		GS	Eighteen Little Preludes and Fugues (No. 14)
		GS	Short Preludes and Fugues (pg. 8)
		P	Short Preludes and Fugues (pg. 10)
		Sch	Little Bach Book (No. 7)

Composer	Title	Publisher	Volume or Collection
BACH, J. S. (Cont.)	Little Prelude in D Minor	K	Various Short Preludes and Fugues (pg. 18)
		GS	Short Preludes and Fugues (pg. 16)
		P	Short Preludes and Figures (pg. 20)
	Little Prelude in E Minor	K	Various Short Preludes and Fugues (pg. 10)
		GS	Eighteen Little Preludes and Fugues (No. 10)
		GS	Short Preludes and Fugues (pg. 8)
		P	(pg. 10)
	Little Prelude in F	K	Various Short Preludes and Fugues (pg. 11)
			Eighteen Little Preludes and Fugues (No. 11) (Key of E-flat)
		GS	Short Preludes and Fugues (pg. 9)
		P	(pg. 11)
		K	First Bach Book (pg. 26)
		Sch	Little Piano Book of Wilhelm Friedemann Bach (No. 7)
		GS	Master Series for the Young (pg. 26)
		CF	Road to Piano Artistry, Vol. IV (Scionti)
		U	Old Masters for Young Pianists (Kuranda)
	Little Prelude in G Minor	K	Various Short Preludes and Fugues (pg. 13)
		GS	Short Preludes and Fugues (pg. 11)
		P	(pg. 14)
		K	First Bach Book (No. 23)
		Sch	Little Piano Book of Wilhelm Friedemann Bach (No. 9)
	Marche in E-flat	K	Little Notebook of Anna Magdalena Bach (pg. 72)
		K	First Bach Book (No. 17)
		GS	First Lessons in Bach, Bk. I (Carroll)
		CF	Bach First Lessons, Bk. I (Carroll)
		GS	Master Series for the Young
	Menuet in C Minor	K	French Suites
		P	
		GS	
		BMC	Bach for Early Grades, Bk. III
	Polonaise in F	K	Little Notebook of Anna Magdalena Bach (pg. 51)
		P	Notenbuch der Anna Magdalena Bach
	Polonaise in G	K	Little Notebook of Anna Magdalena Bach (pg. 82)
		CF	Bach First Lessons, Bk. II
	Polonaise in G Minor	K	Little Notebook of Anna Magdalena Bach (pg. 66)
		P	Notenbuch der Anna Magdalena Bach (No. 14)

Composer	Title	Publisher	Volume or Collection
BACH, J. S. (Cont.)		CF	Bach First Lessons, Bk. II (Carroll) (No. 1)
		GS	First Lessons in Bach, Bk. II (Carroll) (No. 1)
		GS	Master Series for the Young (pg. 24)
	Polonaise in G Minor	K	Little Notebook of Anna Magdalena Bach (pg. 62)
		P	Notenbuch der Anna Magdalena Bach (No. 12)
		CF	Bach First Lessons, Bk. II (Carroll) (No. 6)
		GS	First Lessons in Bach, Bk. II (Carroll) (No. 6)
BACH, W. F. (1710-1784)	Allegro in A	SG	Classics from the 17th and 18th Centuries (Tapper)
		Su	Recital Repertoire, Bk. II (Podolsky)
BENDA, F. (1709-1786)	Sonatina in D Minor	Sch	Simple Short Piano Pieces
		GS	Introduction to Piano Classics, Vol. II (Mirovitch)
	Sonatina in G	Sch	Simple Short Piano Pieces
		GS	Introduction to Piano Classics, Vol. II (Mirovitch)
BYRD, W. (1542 or '43-1623)	Galiardo in A Minor	GS	Early Keyboard Music, Vol. I
	Pavanne (From "The Earl of Salisbury")	GS	Early Keyboard Music, Vol. I
		B	Hours with the Masters, Bk. III
		PP	Hundred Best Short Classics, Bk. II
	Preludium in C	GS	Early Keyboard Music, Vol. I
CHAMBONNIÈRES, J. C. de (1602-1670)	Sarabande in G	GS	Early Keyboard Music, Vol. I
CIMAROSA, D (1749-1801)	Sonatas Nos. 2, 5, 9	E	Thirty-two Sonatas, Vol. I
	Sonatas Nos. 13, 15, 16,17	E	Thirty-two Sonatas, Vol. II
CORELLI, A. (1653-1713)	Gavotte in G	Su	Recital Repertoire, Bk. IV (Podolsky)
COUPERIN, F. (1668-1733)	La Commére	B	Hours with the Masters, Bk. IV
	Le Moucheron	B	Hours with the Masters, Bk. III
	Les Moissonneurs	GS	Early Keyboard Music, Vol. II
		BH	Airs and Dances, Bk. I (Dorolle)
		A	Beringer's School of Easy Classics: Old English and French Masters
DANDRIEU, A. (1684-1740)	Le Timpanon	BH	Airs and Dances, Bk. I (Dorolle)
	The Whirlwinds	Su	Recital Repertoire, Bk. II (Podolsky)

Composer	Title	Publisher	Volume or Collection
DAQUIN, C. (1694-1772)	La Melodieuse	BH	Airs and Dances, Bk. II
DITTERSDORF, K. (1739-1799)	Allegro in E	Sch	Simple Short Piano Pieces (Kreutz) (No. 9)
DUSSEK, J. L. (1760-1812)	Larghetto quasi andante	EV	New Recital Repertoire (Mirovitch)
	Sonatina, Op, 20, No. 1 Allegro non tanto Rondo	GS	Album of Sonatinas
	Sonatina, Op. 20, No. 2 Allegretto quasi andante Rondo	Wo	Sonatina Album, Bk. II
	Sonatina, Op. 20, No. 3 Allegro quasi presto Rondo	GS	Selected Sonatinas, Bk. II
FISCHER, J. K. F. (1650-1746)	Gigue in G	Sch	Notebook of Johann Kaspar Ferd. Fischer
	Fughette in D		
	Fugue in A Minor	K	A Little Book of Fugues (No. 3)
	Fugue in A Minor		(No. 4)
	Fugue in F		(No. 14)
	Fugue in G Minor		(No. 9)
FLEISCHER, F. G. (1722-1806)	Minuetto in F	Sch	Menuetten fürs Clavier
	Minuetto I in G		
	Minuetto II in G		
FRESCOBALDI, G. (1583-1644)	Corrente	B	Hours with the Masters, Bk. III
	Gagliarda in G Minor	GS	Early Keyboard Music, Bk. I
GALUPPI, B. (1706-1785)	Sonata	TP	Eighteenth Century Italian Keyboard Music
GEMINIANI, F. (1687-1762)	Allegro in A	Su	Recital Repertoire, Bk. IV (Podolsky)
GRAUN, C. H (1701-1759)	Andante in F	U	Grosse Meister für kleine Hände
GRAUPNER, C. (1683-1760)	Air en Gavotte in D	P	Contemporaries of Telemann (No. 9)
GRÉTRY, A. E. (1741-1813)	Gigue in E-flat	A	Beringer's School of Easy Classics: Old English and French Masters
GRIECO (1680-?)	Aria di Ballo	HC	Clavecinistes Italiens (No. 6)

Composer	Title	Publisher	Volume or Collection
GROSSE, M. C. (2nd half of 18th century)	Minuetto I in A	Sch	Minuetten fürs Clavier
	Minuetto II in A		
HANDEL, G. F. (1685-1759)	Air in D Minor (From Suite X)	P	Handel Suites, Vol. I
		K	Handel Suites, Vol. II
	Air in G Minor	Sch	Pieces for Harpsichord, Vol. I (No. 25)
		Su	Recital Repertoire, Bk. I (Podolsky)
	Allegro in G Major	PP	Hundred Best Short Classics, Bk. V
	A tempo guisto	Sch	Pieces for Harpsichord, Vol. I (No. 27)
	Chaconne in G (From Chaconne with 62 Variations)	GS	Master Series for the Young
	Chaconne in G Minor	Sch	Pieces for Harpsichord, Vol. I (No. 5)
	Courante in F Major	PP	Hundred Best Short Classics, Bk. II
		GS	Handel: 12 Easy Pieces
		B	Hours with the Masters, Bk. II
		H	Easiest Original Pieces
		BH	Airs and Dances, Bk. II (Dorolle)
	Fuga in G	Sch	Aylesford Pieces (No. 5)
		Sch	Pieces for Harpsichord, Vol. II (No. 50)
	Gavotte in G	Sch	Aylesford Pieces (No. 3)
		Sch	Pieces for Harpsichord, Vol. I (No. 6)
	Gavotte in C	H	Easiest Original Pieces
		GS	Handel: 12 Easy Pieces
	Gavotte in G Minor		Pieces for Harpsichord, Vol. I (No. 24)
	Gigue in G	Su	Recital Repertoire, Bk. I (Podolsky)
	Impertinence	Sch	Aylesford Pieces (No. 6)
		Sch	Pieces for Harpsichord, Vol. II (No. 51)
	Little Fugue in C (No. I)	GS	Master Series for the Young
	Little Sonata in C	U	Old Masters for Young Pianists (Kuranda)
	Menuet in A Minor	Sch	Pieces for Harpsichord, Vol. II (No. 67)
	Menuet in D	Sch	Vol. I (No. 30)
	Menuet in F		(No. 9)
	Menuet in G Minor		(No. 65)
	Menuetto in B-flat (From Suite in B-flat)	K	Suites and Chaconnes, Vol. II
	Minuet in F	Sch	Pieces for Harpsichord, Vol. II (No. 60)
		Sch	Aylesford Pieces (No. 14)
	Minuet in F Minor	Sch	Pieces for Harpsichord, Vol. II (No. 59)

Composer	Title	Publisher	Volume or Collection
HANDEL, G. F. (Cont.)		Sch	Aylesford Pieces (No. 15)
	Minuet in G Minor	Sch	Pieces for Harpsichord, Vol. I (No. 29)
	Prelude in G	GS	Master Series for the Young
		He	A Treasury of Easy Classics (Abrams)
	Sarabande in D Minor (From Suite XI)	P	Handel Suites, Vol. II
		K	Handel Suites and Chaconnes, Vol. II
		GS	Handel: 12 Easy Pieces
		U	Old Masters for Young Pianists (Kuranda)
		H	Easiest Original Pieces
		CF	Road to Piano Artistry, Vol. VI (Scionti)
		GS	Master Series for the Young
	Sarabande in D Minor (From Suite XV)	P	Suites, Vol. II
	Sarabande in E Minor (From Suite IV)	P	Suites, Vol. I
		K	Suites and Chaconnes, Vol. I
	Sarabande in E	Sch	Pieces for Harpsichord, Vol. II (No. 16)
	Sarabande in F		(No. 23)
	Sarabande in G Minor (From Suite VII)	P	Suites, Vol. I
		K	Suites and Chaconnes, Vol. I
	Sonatina in B-flat	BH	Airs and Dances, Bk. II (Dorolle)
		H	Easiest Original Pieces
		GS	Handel: 12 Easy Pieces
		GS	Master Series for the Young
	Suite XI in D Minor Allemande Courante Sarabande Gigue	P	Suites, Vol. II
		K	Suites and Chaconnes, Vol. II
	Toccata in G Minor	Sch	Pieces for Harpsichord, Vol. I (No. 26)
		Sch	Aylesford Pieces (No. 4)
HÄSSLER, J. W. (1747-1822)	Minuetto I in A	Sch	Menuetten fürs Clavier
	Minuetto II in A		
HAYDN, J. (1732-1809)	Finale: Allegro (From Sonata in C, No. 5)	P	Haydn Sonatas, Vol. I
		K	Haydn Sonatas, Vol. I
		GS	Haydn Sonatas, Vol. I
		GS	Master Series for the Young
	Finale: Presto (From Sonata in A, No. 33)	P	Haydn Sonatas, Vol. III
	La Roxalane (Air Varie)	K	Haydn: 8 Various Compositions for Piano
		H	Easiest Original Pieces
		A	Beringer's School of Easy Classics: Haydn
		GS	Master Series for the Young

Composer	Title	Publisher	Volume or Collection
HAYDN, J. (Cont.)		EV	New Recital Repertoire (Mirovitch)
	Menuetto (From Sonata in A)	P	Haydn Sonatas, Vol. III (No. 33)
	Menuetto (From Sonata in B-flat)	P	Haydn Sonatas, Vol. II (No. 22)
		H	Easiest Original Pieces
	Menuetto: Moderato (From Sonata in C-sharp minor)	P	Haydn Sonatas, Vol. I (No. 6)
		K	Haydn Sonatas, Vol. I (No. 6)
		GS	Haydn Sonatas, Vol. I (No. 6)
	Menuetto (From Sonata in E)	P	Haydn Sonatas, Vol. II (No. 18)
		K	Haydn Sonatas, Vol. II (No. 17)
		GS	Haydn Sonatas, Vol. II (No. 17)
		GS	Master Series for the Young
	Scherzando (From Sonata in C-sharp minor)	P	Haydn Sonatas, Vol. I (No. 6)
		K	Haydn Sonatas, Vol. I (No. 6)
		GS	Haydn Sonatas, Vol. I (No. 6)
	Sonatina in C Allegro Andante Menuet	P	Six Little Divertimenti (No. 1)
	Sonatina in C Allegro Andante Menuet	P	Six Little Divertimenti (No. 2)
	Sonatina in C Moderato Menuet Finale	AMP	Haydn: Six Sonatinas (No. 5)
		P	Haydn Sonatas, Vol. IV (No. 43)
	Sonatina in D Allegro Menuetto	AMP	Haydn: Six Sonatinas (No. 1)
		H	Easiest Original Pieces
		P	Six Little Divertimenti (No. 3)
	Sonatina in F Allegro Scherzo	AMP	Haydn: Six Sonatinas (No. 4) Six Little Divertimenti (No. 6)
	Sonatina in G Presto Andante Menuet	AMP	Haydn: Six Sonatinas (No. 6)
		P	Haydn Sonatas, Vol. I (No. 11)
HILLER, J. A. (1728-1804)	Minuet in A	GS	Introduction to Piano Classics, Vol. II (Mirovitch)
KIRNBERGER, J. P (1721-1783)	Gavotte in D	Sch	Clavierstücke für Anfänger
	Gavotte in D Minor	K	Old Masters of the 16th, 17th and 18th Centuries
		SU	Recital Repertoire, Bk, I (Podolsky)

Composer	Title	Publisher	Volume or Collection
KIRNBERGER, J. P. (Cont.)	La Lutine in A	K	Old Masters of the 16th, 17th and 18th Centuries
	Menuet in D	K	Old Masters of the 16th, 17th and 18th Centuries
	Passepied in E *andante*	GS	Introduction to Piano Classics, Vol. I (Mirovitch)
	Polonaise in D	GS	Introduction to Piano Classics, Vol. I (Mirovitch)
	Polonaise in G Minor	K	Old Masters of the 16th, 17th and 18th Centuries
KREBS, J. (1713-1780)	Allegro in G	Sch GS	Simple Short Piano Pieces Introduction to Piano Classics, Vol. II (Mirovitch)
	Bourrée in E-flat	U	Grosse Meister für kleine Hände
	Bourrée in G Minor	P	Contemporaries of Telemann
	Toccata in E-flat (Allegro)	GS Sch	Introduction to Piano Classics, Vol. II (Mirovitch) Simple Short Piano Pieces
KUHNAU, J. (1660-1722)	Praeludium in E Minor (From Suite III)	GS GS	Early Keyboard Music, Bk. I Introduction to Piano Classics, Vol. II (Mirovitch)
	Sarabande (From Suite III)	GS	Early Keyboard Music, Bk. I
LOEILLET, J. (1653-1728)	Sarabande in A	H	Contemporaries of Purcell
MARPURG, F. W. (1718-1795)	Menuet in G	K	Old Masters of the 16th, 17th and 18th Centuries
	Prélude in G	BH	Airs and Dances, Bk. II (Dorolle)
MARTINI, G. (1706-1784)	Gavotte in F Major	K PP	Old Masters of the 16th, 17th and 18th Centuries Hundred Best Classics, Bk. III
MATTHESON, J. (1681-1764)	Menuett (From Suite V in C Minor)	GS	Early Keyboard Music, Bk. II
MONN (MANN) J. C. (1726-1782)	Siciliana	U	Grosse Meister für kleine Hände
MOURET, J. J. (1682-1735)	Bourrée in E	A	Beringer's School of Easy Classics: Old English and French Masters
MOZART, W. A. (1756-1791)	Adagio in A	Sch MMC H	Six Viennese Sonatinas (No. 2)
	Adagio in C	Sch	Six Viennese Sonatinas (No. 1)

Composer	Title	Publisher	Volume or Collection
MOZART, W. A. (Cont.)		MMC H	
	Allegro Grazioso	GS	Master Series for the Young
	Allegro in C (K 6)	Sch	Notebook for Nannerl Mozart
	Andante in D	Sch MMC H	Six Viennese Sonatinas (No. 3)
	Andante in G (K 545)	K P GS	Mozart Sonatas Mozart Sonatas Master Series for the Young
	Menuetto in A	Sch MMC H	Six Viennese Sonatinas (No. 2)
	Menuetten I and II (K 282)	K P B K	Mozart Sonatas Mozart Sonatas Hours with the Masters, Bk. IV Easy Compositions by Mozart and Beethoven
	Menuetto in C	Sch MMC CF	Six Viennese Sonatinas (No. 6) Road to Piano Artistry, Vol. VIII (Scionti)
	Menuetto in D	Sch MMC H K	Six Viennese Sonatinas (No. 3) Easy Compositions by Mozart and Beethoven
	Mio Caro Adone (K 180)	K	Easy Compositions by Mozart and Beethoven
	Rondo in C (K 545)	K P GS B	Mozart Sonatas Mozart Sonatas Master Series for the Young Hours with the Masters, Bk. II
	Rondo in D	Sch	The Young Mozart
	Sonata in C (K 545) Allegro Andante Rondo	K P	Mozart Sonatas Mozart Sonatas
	Sonatina in F	Sch MMC H	Six Viennese Sonatinas (No. 5)
MUFFAT, G. T. (1690-1770)	Capriccio desperato	Sch	Partiten und Stücke
	Gavotte (From Partita in C Minor)		
	Harlequin		
	Menuet (From Partita in C)		

Composer	Title	Publisher	Volume or Collection
MUFFAT, G. T. (Cont.)	Menuet, From Partita in C Minor		
	Menuet in B-flat	GS	Introduction to Piano Classics, Vol. III (Mirovitch)
	Menuet in D	P	Contemporaries of Telemann
	Prelude, (From Partita in C)	Sch	Partiten und Stücke
	Rigaudon in C	U	Grosse Meister für kleine Hände
	Sarabande, (From Partita in C Minor)	Sch	Partiten und Stücke
	Siciliana	Sch	Partiten und Stücke
MURCHHAUSER, F. (1663-1738)	Fugue in C Major, No. 2	K	A Little Book of Fugues
NEEFE, C. G. (1748-1798)	Minuetto in F	Sch	Menuetten fürs Clavier
NICHELMANN, C. (1717-1762)	Sarabande in C Minor	K	Old Masters of the 16th, 17th and 18th Centuries
PARADIS, M. T. (1759-1824)	Sicilienne	Su	Recital Repertoire, Bk. III (Podolsky)
PESCETTI, G. B. (1704-1766)	Allegretto in C	HC	Clavecinistes Italiens (No. 4)
PURCELL, H. (1658-1695)	Air in G Minor	H	Contemporaries of Purcell
	Hornpipe in E Minor	PP	Frederick Moore Collection
		He	A Little Treasury of Classics, Bk. IV (Lambert)
	Intrada and March, (From Suite in C, No. 5)	GS GS Su	Purcell: Keyboard Suites Early Keyboard Music, Vol. I Recital Repertoire, Bk. I (Podolsky)
	Minuet, (From Suite in F, No. 8)	GS GS	Purcell: Keyboard Suites Early Keyboard Music, Vol. I
	Riggadoon, (From Suite in C, No. 5)	GS GS	Purcell: Keyboard Suites Early Keyboard Suites, Vol. I
	Suite in G, No. 1 Prelude Almand Courante Minuet	GS GS	Purcell: Keyboard Suites Early Keyboard Music, Vol. I
RAMEAU, J. P. (1683-1764)	La Joyeuse	B	Hours with the Masters, Bk. IV
	Les Tendres Plaintes	BH GS	Airs and Dances, Bk. II (Dorolle) Early Keyboard Music, Bk. II

Composer	Title	Publisher	Volume or Collection
RAMEAU, J. P. (Cont.)		A	Beringer's School of Easy Classics: Old English and French Masters
	Rigaudon in E Minor	GS	Early Keyboard Music, Bk. II
		B	Hours with the Masters, Bk. II
		K	Old Masters of the 16th, 17th and 18th Centuries
	Tambourin	A	Beringer's School of Easy Classics: Old English and French Masters
		GS	Early Keyboard Music, Bk. II
		PP	Hundred Best Short Classics, Bk. III
		He	A Little Treasury of Classics, Bk. II (Lambert)
		GS	Published Separately
REICHARDT, J. F. (1752-1814)	Aria in G Minor	EV	New Recital Repertoire (Mirovitch)
	Scherzando in D	GS	Introduction to Piano Classics, Vol. II (Mirovitch)
ROSSI, M. A. de (1720-1794)	Allegro sostenuto	HC	Clavecinistes Italiens (No. 1)
RUTINI, G. M. (1730-1797)	Menuetto in C	TP	Eighteenth Century Italian Keyboard Music
		HC	Clavecinistes Italiens (No. 7)
SACCHINI, A. (1734-1786)	Sonata per il Cembalo	TP	Eighteenth Century Italian Keyboard Music
SANDER, F. S. (1760-1796)	Sonatina in G Allegretto Larghetto Allegro ma non troppo	Sch	Clavier Sonatinen (Kreutz)
SARTI, G. (1729-1802)	Allegro piuttosto moderato	HC	Clavecinistes Italiens
SCARLATTI, D. (1685-1757)	Air with Variations in A Minor	A	Beringer's School of Easy Classics: Scarlatti
		Su	Recital Repertoire, Bk. I (Podolsky)
	Allegro in D	He	A Treasury of Easy Classics (Abrams)
	Allegretto in E Minor	A	Beringer's School of Easy Classics: Scarlatti
	Minuetto in B-flat	He	A Treasury of Easy Classics (Abrams)
	Siciliano in D Minor	PP	Hundred Best Short Classics, Bk. I
	Siciliano in F	A	Beringer's School of Easy Classics: Scarlatti
	Sonatas 1. D Minor (L 423) 2. G (L 83)	M	Twelve Easy Scarlatti Sonatas (Mirovitch)

Composer	Title	Publisher	Volume or Collection
SCARLATTI, D. (Cont.)	3. G (L 79) 5. B-flat (L 97)		
SCHILLING, F. W. (2nd half of 18th Century)	Sonatina in B-flat Andantino Allegro	Sch	Clavier Sonatinen (Kreutz)
TELEMANN, G. P. (1681-1767)	Aria (From G Major Partita)	P	Contemporaries of Telemann
	Bourrée in A	P	Contemporaries of Telemann
	Bourrée in E-flat	Su	Recital Repertoire, Bk. II (Podolsky)
	Fantasia in D, No. I	Sch EV	Telemann: Kleine Fantasien New Recital Repertoire (Mirovitch)
	Fantasia in F	Sch	Notebook for Wolfgang
	Gavotte(From Overture in A Minor)	P	Contemporaries of Telemann
	Presto in G	GS	Introduction to Piano Classics, Vol. II (Mirovitch)
	Rigaudon I, II	P	Contemporaries of Telemann
TÜRK, D. G. (TUERK) (1750-1813)	Andantino in F	Sch	Simple Short Piano Pieces
WITTHAUER, J. G. (1750-1802)	Menuetto in F	Sch	Menuetten fürs Clavier
	Sonate in B-flat Poco moderato ed affetuoso Larghetto Allegro scherzando	Sch	Clavier Sonatinen (Kreutz)
WOLF, E. W. (1735-1792)	Sonatina in C Minor Larghetto Allegretto	Sch	Clavier Sonatinen (Kreutz)
WOLF. G. F. (1762-1814)	Sonatina in D Allegretto grazioso Menuetto con Trio Allegro scherzando	Sch	Clavier Sonatinen (Kreutz)
ZIPOLI, D. (1675-1726)	Aria in B Minor	K	Old Masters of the 16th, 17th and 18th Centuries
	Gavotta	HC	Clavecinistes Italiens
	Preludio in B Minor	K	Old Masters of the 16th, 17th and 18th Centuries

Composer	Title	Publisher	Volume or Collection
BEETHOVEN, L. van (1770-1827)	Adieu to the Piano	GS	Published Separately
	Bagatelle in A, Op. 119, No. 4	K P K H	Various Piano Pieces Various Pieces Easy Compositions by Mozart and Beethoven Easiest Original Pieces
	Bagatelle in A, Op. 119, No. 10	K P H	Various Piano Pieces Various Pieces Easiest Original Pieces
	Bagatelle in A Minor, Op. 119, No. 9	K P H	Various Piano Pieces Various Pieces Easiest Original Pieces
	Bagatelle in D, Op. 119, No. 3	K P H CF PP	Various Piano Pieces Various Pieces Easiest Original Pieces Road to Piano Artistry, Vol. V (Scionti) Hundred Best Short Classics, Bk. II
	Bagatelle in F, Op. 33, No. 3	K P B GS	Various Piano Pieces Various Pieces Hours with the Masters, Bk. II Beethoven: Easy Compositions
	German Dance in C	P	Ecossaisen und Deutche Tänze (No. 12)
	German Dance in D		(No. 10)
	German Dance in F		(No. 9)
	German Dance in G		(No. 11)
	Ländler in D	K	Easy Compositions by Mozart and Beethoven
	Ländriche Tänze	GS	Beethoven: Seven Ländriche Tänze
	Minuet in D	H	Easiest Original Pieces (No. 3)
	Six Easy Variations on a Swiss Song	K GS K GS	Variations, Vol. II Easy Compositions by Mozart and Beethoven Master Series for the Young

	Sonata in G, Op. 49, No. 2
	  Allegro ma non troppo
	
	  Tempo di Minuetto
		K
		P
		SS
		GS
		Ox
		GS
		CF
			Sonatas, Vol. II
			
			Thirty-two Sonatinas and Rondos,
			
			Album of Sonatinas
			Road to Piano Artistry, Vol. VII
			   (Scionti)

Composer	Title	Publisher	Volume or Collection
BEETHOVEN, L. (Cont.)	Sonatina in C Allegro Adagio	K P	Sonatinas
	Waltz in F	Sch	Kleine Tänze (Frey) (No. 12)
BORODIN, A. (1834-1887)	Au Convent	GS GS GS	Published Separately Petite Suite Introduction to Piano Classics, Vol. II (Mirovitch)
	Reverie	GS GS	Published Separately Petite Suite
BRAHMS, J. (1833-1897)	Waltz in A-flat, Op. 39, No. 15	GS P K	Waltzes, Op. 39
	Waltz in D Minor, Op. 39, No. 9	GS P K H	Waltzes, Op. 39 Contemporaries of Schumann
	Waltz in G Sharp Minor, Op. 39, No. 3	GS P K	Waltzes, Op. 39
CHOPIN, F. (1810-1849)	Mazurka in B-flat, Op. 7, No. 1	GS K P CF GS GS	Mazurkas Road to Piano Artistry, Vol. VIII (Scionti) Master Series for the Young Chopin Album
	Mazurka in F, Op. 68, No. 3	GS K P GS	Mazurkas Master Series for the Young
	Prelude in B Minor, Op. 28, No. 6	GS K P GS H PP He GS	Preludes, Op. 28 Master Series for the Young Easiest Original Pieces Hundred Best Short Classics, Bk. IV Little Treasury of Classics, Bk. IV Selected Piano Solos by Romantic Composers, Bk. II
	Prelude in E Minor, Op. 28, No. 4	GS K P H PP GS	Preludes Op. 28 Easiest Original Pieces Hundred Best Short Classics, Bk. IV Selected Piano Solos by Romantic Composers, Bk. II

Composer	Title	Publisher	Volume or Collection
CLEMENTI, M. (1752-1832)	Rondo in G (From Op. 36, No. 5)	GS GS P	Clementi: Six Sonatinas, Op. 36 Album of Sonatinas Clementi: Sonatinas

	Sonatina in B-flat, Op. 38, No. 2
	  Allegro
	  Moderato
	  Rondo
		GS
		P
			Clementi Sonatinas
			Clementi Sonatinas, Op. 36, 37, 38

	Sonatina in C, Op. 36, No.3
	  Spiritoso
	  Un poco adagio
	  Allegro
		GS
		P
		
		GS
		GS
			Clementi: Six Sonatinas, Op. 36
			Clementi Sonatinas, Op. 36, 37, 38
			
			Album of Sonatinas
			Thirty-two Sonatinas and Rondos

	Sonatina in C, Op. 37, No. 3
	  Allegro
	  Spiritoso
	  Allegro
		GS
		P
			Clementi Sonatinas
			Clementi Sonatinas, Op. 36, 37, 38

	Sonatina in C, Op. 38, No. 1
	  Allegro
	  Tempo di Minuetto
		GS
		P
			Clementi Sonatinas
			Clementi Sonatinas, Op. 36, 37, 38

	Sonatina in E-flat, Op. 37, No. 1
	  Andantino
	  Presto
		GS
		P
			Clementi Sonatinas
			Clementi Sonatinas, Op. 36, 37, 38

	Sonatina in F, Op. 36, No. 4
	  Con spirito
	  Andante con espressione
	  Rondo: Allegro vivace
		GS
		GS
		GS
		CF
			Clementi: Six Sonatinas, Op. 36
			Album of Sonatinas
			Thirty-two Sonatinas and Rondos
			Road to Piano Artistry, Vol. V (Scionti)

	Waltz in C	P	Sonatinen Vorstufe (Preparatory Sonatina Album)
	Waltz in E-flat	EV	New Recital Repertoire (Mirovitch)
FIELD, J. (1782-1837)	Nocturne in B-flat	GS GS Su	Field: Eighteen Nocturnes Published Separately Recital Repertoire, Bk. III (Podolsky)
GADE, N. (1817-1890)	Album-Leaf (From Three Album-Leaves)	H	Contemporaries of Schumann
	Barcarolle, Op. 19, No. 5	CF	Road to Piano Artistry, Vol. V (Scionti)
	Elegie, Op. 19, No. 1	B	Hours with the Masters, Bk. III (Podolsky)
GRIEG, E. (1843-1907)	Album Leaf, Op. 28, No. 2	GS P GS	Album Leaves, Op. 28 Grieg: 45 Selected Compositions, Bk. II
	Anitra's Dance, Op. 46, No. 3	GS P	Peer Gynt Suite I, Op. 46
	Ase's Death, Op. 46, No. 2		

Composer	Title	Publisher	Volume or Collection
GRIEG, E. (Cont.)	At Thy Feet, Op. 68, No. 3	GS P	Lyrical Pieces, Op. 68
		GS	Grieg: 45 Selected Compositions, Bk. I
	Bell Ringing, Op. 54, No. 6	GS P	Lyrical Pieces, Op. 54
		GS	Grieg: 45 Selected Compositions, Bk. I
		GS	Published Separately
	Berceuse, Op. 38, No. 1	GS P	Lyrical Pieces, Op. 38
		GS	Grieg: 45 Selected Compositions, Bk. I
		GS	Selected Piano Solos by Romantic Composers, Vol. II
	Canon, Op. 38, No. 8	GS P	Lyrical Pieces, Op. 38
		GS	Grieg: 45 Selected Compositions, Bk. II
	Dance Caprice, Op. 28, No. 3	GS P	Lyrical Pieces, Op. 28
		GS	Grieg: 45 Selected Compositions, Bk. I
		GS	Published Separately
	Elegie, Op. 38, No. 6	GS P	Lyrical Pieces, Op. 38
		GS	Grieg: 45 Selected Compositions, Bk. I
	Elegie, Op. 47, No. 7	GS P	Lyrical Pieces, Op. 47
		GS	Grieg: 45 Selected Compositions, Bk. II
	Elfin Dance, Op. 12, No. 4	GS P	Lyrical Pieces, Op. 12
		GS	Grieg: 45 Selected Compositions, Bk. I
		GS	Master Series for the Young
		CF	Road to Piano Artistry, Vol. III (Scionti)
		GS	Published Separately
	Erotik, Op. 43, No. 5	GS P	Lyrical Pieces, Op. 43
		GS	Published Separately
	Folk-Song, Op. 12, No. 5	GS P	Lyrical Pieces, Op. 12
		GS	Grieg: 45 Selected Compositions, Bk. I
		GS	Master Series for the Young
		He	A Treasury of Easy Classics (Abrams)
	Folk-Song, Op. 38, No. 2	GS P	Lyrical Pieces, Op. 38
		GS	Grieg: 45 Selected Compositions, Bk. I
		GS	Master Series for the Young

Composer	Title	Publisher	Volume or Collection
GRIEG, E. (Cont.)	In My Native Country, Op. 43, No. 3	GS P	Lyrical Pieces, Op. 43
		GS	Grieg: 45 Selected Compositions, Bk. I
	In the Hall of the Mountain King, Op. 46, No. 4	GS P	Peer Gynt Suite I, Op. 46
		GS	Published Separately
	Little Bird, Op. 43, No. 4	GS P	Lyrical Pieces, Op. 43
		CF	Road to Piano Artistry, Vol. IV (Scionti)
		GS	Published Separately
	Melody, Op. 38, No. 3	GS P	Lyrical Pieces, Op. 38
		GS	Grieg: 45 Selected Compositions, Bk. II
	Melody, Op. 47, No. 3	GS P	Lyrical Pieces, Op. 47
	Morning Mood, Op. 46, No. 1	GS P	Peer Gynt Suite I, Op. 46
		GS	Published Separately
	Norwegian Bridal Procession, Op. 19, No. 2	GS P	Sketches of Norwegian Life, Op. 19
		GS	Grieg: 45 Selected Compositions, Bk. II
	Norwegian Dance, Op. 38, No. 4	GS P	Lyrical Pieces, Op. 38
	Norwegian Dance, Op. 47, No. 4	GS P	Lyrical Pieces, Op. 47
	Norwegian Melody, Op. 12, No. 6	GS P	Lyrical Pieces, Op. 12
		GS	Grieg: 45 Selected Compositions, Bk. I
		GS	Master Series for the Young
	Notturno, Op. 54, No. 4	GS P	Lyrical Pieces, Op. 54
		GS	Grieg: 45 Selected Compositions, Bk. II
		GS	Published Separately
	Papillons (Butterfly), Op. 43, No. 1	GS P	Lyrical Pieces, Op. 43
		GS	Grieg: 45 Selected Compositions, Bk. I
		GS	Published Separately
	Sailor's Song, Op. 68, No. 1	GS P	Lyrical Pieces, Op. 68
		GS	Master Series for the Young
		GS	Published Separately
	Skip Dance, Op. 38, No. 5	GS P	Lyrical Pieces, Op. 68
		GS	Master Series for the Young

Composer	Title	Publisher	Volume or Collection
GRIEG, E. (Cont.)	Solitary Traveller (Solitary Wanderer), Op. 43, No. 2	GS P	Lyrical Pieces, Op. 43
		GS	Grieg: 45 Selected Compositions. Bk. I
		CF	Road to Piano Artistry, Vol. VI (Scionti)
		GS	Published Separately
	Solvejg's Songs, Op. 55, No. 4	GS P	Peer Gynt Suite II, Op. 55
		GS	Master Series for the Young
	Waltz, Op. 38, No. 7	GS P	Lyrical Pieces, Op. 38
		GS	Grieg: 45 Selected Compositions, Bk. I
		GS	Selected Piano Solos by Romantic Composers, Bk. III
GURLITT, C. (1820-1901)	Barcarolle, Op. 131, No. 22	GS	Twenty-four Melodious Studies, Op. 131
	Evening Piece, Op. 131, No. 20		
HELLER, S. (1813-1888)	From "Fifty Selected Studies" 11. Interlude, Op. 47, No. 20 14. Tally-Ho, Op. 47, No. 18 17. Joyous Song, Op. 45, No. 4 19. Village Dance Op. 45, No. 20 24. The Warrior's Song Op. 45, No. 15 27. Spinning Song, Op. 45, No. 19 28. Sailing Along Op. 45, No. 23 29. Wind in the Wheatfield, Op. 45, No. 24 30. Epilogue, Op. 45, No. 25 31. Without A Care, Op. 46, No. 1 33. The Bees, Op. 46, No. 5 36. Song Without Words, Op. 46, No. 8 37. The Spinning Top, Op. 46, No. 10 39. The Mountain Cascade, Op. 46, No. 12 40. Punchinello, Op. 46, No. 16 41. On the Riviera, Op. 46, No. 17 42. The Blacksmith, Op. 46, No. 18 43. In A Swing, Op. 46, No. 19 44. The New Bicycle, Op. 46, No. 21	GS	Fifty Selected Studies, From Op. 45, 46, 47

Composer	Title	Publisher	Volume or Collection
HELLER, S. (Cont.)	45. Drummer Boy, Op. 46, No. 23		
	46. With Cap and Bells, Op. 46, No. 24		
	47. Boat Song, Op. 46, No. 25		
	48. Storm at Sea, Op. 46, No. 26		
	49. The Town Crier, Op. 46, No. 27		
	From "Thirty Progressive Studies," Op. 46	GS R	Thirty Progressive Studies, Op. 46
	1. Without A Care		
	4. Shooting the Rapids		
	5. The Bees		
	8. Song Without Words		
	9. Playing Tag		
	10. The Spinning Top		
	12. The Mountain Cascade		
	14. Gaiety		
	15. Idilio		
	16. Punchinello		
	17. On the Riviera		
	18. The Blacksmith		
	19. In A Swing		
	20. Dwarf's March		
	21. The New Bicycle		
	23. Drummer Boy		
	24. With Cap and Bells		
	25. Boat Song		
	26. Storm at Sea		
	27. The Town Crier		
	28. Smoothly Sailing		
	29. Anticipation		
	From "Twenty Five Melodious Studies," Op. 45	GS R	Twenty Five Melodious Studies, Op. 45
	3. Up and Down the Steps		
	4. Joyous Song		
	6. Shadow Waltz		
	11. Caprice		
	12. Sternness		
	13. Waltz		
	15. The Warrior's Song		
	17. Novelette		
	19. Spinning Song		
	20. Village Dance		
	21. Gnomes		
	22. The Harp		
	23. Sailing Along		
	24. Wind in the Wheatfield		
	25. Epilogue		
	From "Twenty Five Studies," Op. 47	GS R	Twenty Five Studies, Op. 47
	8. Spinning Wheel		
	18. Tally-Ho		

Composer	Title	Publisher	Volume or Collection
HELLER, S. (Cont.)	20. Interlude 22. Express Train 24. Serenity 25. Country Festival		
	Preludes, Op. 81 (Complete)	GS	Twenty-four Preludes, Op. 81
	Prelude in D Minor (Sailing Along), Op. 45, No. 23	CF	Road to Piano Artistry, Vol. VII (Scionti)
		GS R	Twenty Five Melodious Studies, Op. 45
		GS	Fifty Selected Studies from Op. 45, 46, 47 (No. 28)
	Study in A (Spinning Wheel) Op. 47, No. 8	GS	Selected Piano Solos by Romantic Composers, Bk. I
		R GS	Twenty Five Studies, Op. 47
	Warrior's Song, Op. 45, No. 15	GS	Selected Piano Solos by Romantic Composers, Bk. III
		GS R	Twenty Five Studies, Op. 47
		GS	Fifty Selected Studies from Op. 45, 46, 47 (No. 24)
JENSEN, A. (1837-1879)	Dedication, Op. 33	H	Contemporaries of Schumann
	Lied, Op. 33, No. 10	H B	Contemporaries of Schumann Hours with the Masters, Bk. IV
	Longing, Op. 8, No. 5	B	Hours with the Masters, Bk. IV
	Peaceful Afternoon, Op. 17, No. 7	CF	Road to Piano Artistry, Vol. V
	The Little Trumpeter	Su	Recital Repertoire, Bk. I
KUHLAU, F. (1786-1832)	Rondo in A, Op. 40, No. 2	GS	Thirty Two Sonatinas and Rondos
	Sonatina in A Minor, Op. 88, No. 3 Allegro con affetto Andantino Allegro burlesco	GS GS	Kuhlau Sonatinas, Bk. II Thirty Two Sonatinas and Rondos
	Sonatina in C, Op. 20, No. 1 Allegro Andante Rondo	GS GS GS	Kuhlau Sonatinas, Bk. I Album of Sonatinas Thirty Two Sonatinas and Rondos
	Sonatina in C, Op. 55, No. 3 Allegro con spirito Allegretto grazioso	GS GS GS	Kuhlau Sonatinas, Bk. I Album of Sonatinas Thirty Two Sonatinas and Rondos
	Sonatina in C, Op. 55, No. 6 Allegro maestoso Menuet	GS	Kuhlau Sonatinas, Bk. I

Composer	Title	Publisher	Volume or Collection

KUHLAU, F. (Cont.)	Sonatina in C, Op. 88, No. 1
	   Allegro
	   Andantino
	   Rondo
		GS
		GS
			Kuhlau Sonatinas, Bk. II
			Selected Sonatinas, Bk. I

	Sonatina in D, Op. 55, No.5
	   Tempo di Marcia
	   Vivace assai
		GS
		GS
			Kuhlau Sonatinas, Bk. I
			Thirty Two Sonatinas and Rondos

	Sonatina in F, Op. 20, No. 3
	   Allegro quasi presto
	   Rondo
		GS
		GS
		GS
			Kuhlau Sonatinas, Bk. I
			Selected Sonatinas, Bk. II
			Album of Sonatinas

	Sonatina in F, Op. 55, No. 4
	   Allegro ma non tanto
	   Andante con espressione
	   Alla Polacca
		GS
		GS
			Kuhlau Sonatinas, Bk. I
			Thirty Two Sonatinas and Rondos

	Sonatina in F, Op. 88, No. 4
	   Allegro molto
	   Andante con moto
	   Alla Polacca
		GS	Kuhlau Sonatinas, Bk. II

	Sonatina in G, Op. 20, No. 2
	   Allegro
	   Adagio e sostenuto
	   Allegro scherzando
		GS
		GS
		GS
			Kuhlau Sonatinas, Bk. I
			Album of Sonatinas
			Selected Sonatinas, Bk. II

	Sonatina in G, Op. 88, No. 2
	   Allegro assai
	   Andante cantabile
	   Rondo
		GS
		GS
			Kuhlau Sonatinas, Bk. II
			Thirty Two Sonatinas and Rondos

LISZT, F. (1811-1886)	Consolation in E, No. 1	GS
		
		GS
		
		He
		
		PP
			Liszt: Consolations; Liebestraüme
			
			Selected Piano Solos by Romantic
			   Composers, Bk. III
			A Little Treasury of Classics, Bk. IV
			   (Lambert)
			Hundred Best Short Classics, Bk. III

MACDOWELL, E. (1861-1908)	Alla Tarantella, Op. 39, No. 2	BMC	Twelve Etudes, Op. 39
	Hunting Song, Op. 39, No. 1		

	From "New England Idylls,"
	   Op. 62
	   2. Midsummer
	   3. Midwinter
	   4. With Sweet Lavendar
	   5. In Deep Woods
	   6. Indian Idyll
	   7. To an Old White Pine
	   8. From Puritan Days
	   9. From A Log Cabin
		AS	New England Idylls, Op. 62

	From "Woodland Sketches,"
	   Op. 51
	   3. At An Old Trysting
	      Place
		AS	Woodland Sketches, Op. 51

Composer	Title	Publisher	Volume or Collection
MACDOWELL, E. (Cont.)	5. From An Indian Lodge 6. To A Water-Lily 7. From Uncle Remus 8. A Deserted Farm 10. Told At Sunset		
	Romance, Op. 39, No. 3	BMC	Twelve Etudes, Op. 39
	Scotch Poem (Gedichte nach Heinrich Heine, Op. 31, No. 2)	GS	Published Separately
	Sea Pieces, Op. 55 1. To The Sea 2. From A Wandering Iceberg 3. A.D. 1620 4. Starlight 6. From the Depths 7. Nautilus 8. In Midocean	AS	Sea Pieces, Op. 55
MENDELSSOHN, F. (1809-1847)	Allegro in G, Op. 72, No. 1	GS GS He A PP	Six Pieces for Children, Op. 72 Master Series for the Young A Treasury of Easy Classics (Abrams) Beringer's School of Easy Classics: Mendelssohn Hundred Best Short Classics, Bk. III
	Allegretto in G, Op. 72, No. 3	GS GS A PP	Six Pieces for Children, Op. 72 Master Series for the Young Beringer's School of Easy Classics: Mendelssohn Hundred Best Short Classics, Bk. II
	Andante con moto in D, Op. 72, No. 4	GS GS A	Six Pieces for Children, Op. 72 Master Series for the Young Beringer's School of Easy Classics: Mendelssohn
	Andante sostenuto in E-flat, Op. 72, No. 2	GS GS A PP CF	Six Pieces for Children, Op. 72 Master Series for the Young Beringer's School of Easy Classics: Mendelssohn Hundred Best Short Classics, Bk. II Road to Piano Artistry, Vol. IV (Scionti)
	Boat Song, Op. 102, No. 7	GS P GS	Songs Without Words Master Series for the Young
	Confidence, Op. 19, No. 4	GS P GS A GS	Songs Without Words Master Series for the Young Beringer's School of Easy Classics: Mendelssohn Selected Piano Solos by Romantic Composers, Bk. II
	Consolation, Op. 30, No. 3	GS	Songs Without Words

Composer	Title	Publisher	Volume or Collection
MENDELSSOHN, F. (Cont.)		P	
		PP	Hundred Best Short Classics, Bk. II
		GS	Master Series for the Young
		A	Beringer's School of Easy Classics: Mendelssohn
	Faith, Op. 102, No. 6	GS	Songs Without Words
		P	
		GS	Master Series for the Young
	Hope, Op. 38, No. 4	GS	Songs Without Words
		P	
		GS	Master Series for the Young
		GS	Selected Piano Solos by Romantic Composers, Bk. II
	Morning Song, Op. 62, No. 4	GS	Songs Without Words
		P	
		GS	Selected Piano Solos by Romantic Composers, Bk. II
	Regrets, Op. 19, No. 2	GS	Songs Without Words
		P	
		GS	Selected Piano Solos by Romantic Composers, Bk. II
		B	Hours with the Masters, Bk. IV
		GS	Master Series for the Young
	Sadness of Soul, Op. 53, No. 4	GS	Songs Without Words
		P	
	Shepherd's Complaint, Op. 67, No. 5	GS	Songs Without Words
		P	
	Spring Song, Op. 62, No. 6	GS	Songs Without Words
		P	
		GS	Master Series for the Young
		GS	Introduction to Piano Classics, Vol. III (Mirovitch)
	Tarantella, Op. 102, No.3	GS	Songs Without Words
		P	
		GS	Introduction to Piano Classics, Vol. III (Mirovitch)
	Venetian Boat Song I, Op. 19, No. 6	GS	Songs Without Words
		P	
		GS	Master Series for the Young
		GS	Introduction to Piano Classics, Vol. III (Mirovitch)
		A	Beringer's School of Easy Classics: Mendelssohn
	Venetian Boat Song II, Op. 30, No. 6	GS	Songs Without Words
		P	
SCHUBERT, F. (1797-1828)	Deutsch Tänze, Op. 33 (Complete)	P	Schubert Dances
		GS	
	1. A Major	H	Easiest Original Pieces
	2. D Major	H	Easiest Original Pieces
	3. B-flat	H	Easiest Original Pieces

Composer	Title	Publisher	Volume or Collection
SCHUBERT, F. (Cont.)	5. D Major	H	Easiest Original Pieces
		He	A Treasury of Easy Classics (Abrams)
	7. B-flat	H	Easiest Original Pieces
	15. A-flat	Su	Recital Repertoire, Bk. III (Podolsky)
	Ecossaises, Op. 18a (Complete)	P	Schubert Dances
		GS	
		GS	Introduction to Piano Classics, Vol. II (Mirovitch)
	2. D Major	He	A Treasury of Easy Classics (Abrams)
	3. G Major	GS	Master Series for the Young
		He	A Treasury of Easy Classics (Abrams)
	Ländler, Op. 171	P	Schubert Dances
		GS	
	Ländler, Op. posth.	P	Schubert Dances
		GS	
	Ländler in A Minor (From Op. posth.)	He	A Little Treasury of Classics, Bk. II (Lambert)
	Ländler in B-flat		
	Ländler, Op. 67 (Hommage aux Belles Viennoises)	P	Schubert Dances
		GS	
	Menuette, Op. posth. (Eight Minuets) (Complete)	P	Schubert Dances
		GS	
	1. F Major	H	Easiest Original Pieces
	2. C Major	GS	Introduction to Piano Classics, Vol. II (Mirovitch)
	4. F. Major	GS	Introduction to Piano Classics, Vol. II (Mirovitch)
	Two Country Dances (From Op. 171)	H	Easiest Original Pieces
	Waltzes, Op. 9a (18 Waltzes) (Complete)	P	Schubert Dances
		GS	
	1. A-flat	H	Easiest Original Pieces
		GS	Master Series for the Young
		CF	Road to Piano Artistry, Vol. III
	2. A-flat	H	Easiest Original Pieces
		GS	Master Series for the Young
		Su	Recital Repertoire, Bk. III (Podolsky)
		CF	Road to Piano Artistry, Vol. III (Scionti)
	3. A-flat	GS	Master Series for the Young
		CF	Road to Piano Artistry, Vol. III (Scionti)
	6. A-flat	Su	Recital Repertoire, Bk. III (Podolsky)
	Waltzes, Op. 9b (18 Waltzes) (Complete)	P	Schubert Dances
		GS	
	15. F Major	Su	Recital Repertoire, Bk. III (Podolsky) (No. 2)

Composer	Title	Publisher	Volume or Collection
SCHUBERT, F. (Cont.)	17. F Major		(No. 3)
	Waltz in B, Op. 18a, No. 10	P GS	Schubert Dances
	Waltz in B Minor, Op. 18a, No. 9		
	Waltz in D, Op. 18a, No. 5	P GS	Schubert Dances
		GS	Introduction to Piano Classics, Vol. III (Mirovitch)
	Waltz in E-flat, Op. 18a, No. 6	P GS	Schubert Dances
	Waltz in G, Op. 18a, No. 4	P GS	Schubert Dances
		GS	Introduction to Piano Classics, Vol. III (Mirovitch)
	Waltz in G-flat, Op. 18a, No. 7	P GS	Schubert Dances
	Waltzes, Op. 50 (12 Valses sentimentales)	P	Schubert Dances
	4. D Major	He	A Treasury of Easy Classics (Abrams)
	5. D Major	He GS	A Treasury of Easy Classics (Abrams) Master Series for the Young
	12. A-flat	A	Beringer's School of Easy Classics: Schubert
	Waltzes, Op. 91a (12 Grätzer Walzer)	P GS	Schubert Dances
	Waltzes (Selected) Sets I, II and IV	JF	Schubert Dances (Maier)
SCHUMANN, R. (1810-1856)	Andante con espressione Op. 68, No. 26	GS P	Album for the Young, Op. 68
		GS	Master Series for the Young
	Cradle Song, Op. 124, No. 5	GS K GS H	Album Leaves, Op. 124 Complete Works, Vol. VI Master Series for the Young Easiest Original Pieces
	Curious Story, Op. 15, No. 2	AMP GS K GS	Scenes from Childhood, Op. 15 Complete Works, Vol. III Master Series for the Young
	Echoes from the Theater Op. 68, No. 25	GS P	Album for the Young, Op. 68
	From Foreign Lands and Peoples, Op. 15, No. 1	GS AMP K GS PP	Scenes from Childhood, Op. 15 Complete Works, Vol. III Master Series for the Young Hundred Best Short Classics, Bk. IV

Composer	Title	Publisher	Volume or Collection
SCHUMANN, R. (Cont.)	Important Event, Op. 15, No. 6	P GS AMP	Scenes from Childhood, Op. 15
		K	Complete Works, Vol. III
	In Memoriam, Op. 68, No. 28	GS P	Album for the Young, Op. 68
		GS	Master Series for the Young
	Italian Sailor's Song, Op. 68, No. 36	GS P	Album for the Young, Op. 68
		GS	Master Series for the Young
		GS	Selected Piano Solos by Romantic Composers, Bk. II
	Lento assai, Op. 68, No. 30	GS P	Album for the Young, Op. 68
	Lento espressivo, Op. 68, No. 21		
	May Charming May, Op. 68, No. 13	GS P	Album for the Young, Op. 68
		A	Beringer's School of Easy Classics: Schumann
		B	Hours with the Masters, Bk. V
		PP	Hundred Best Short Classics, Bk. IV
	Mignon, Op. 68, No. 35	GS P	Album for the Young, Op. 68
	New Year's Eve, Op. 68, No. 43		
	Norse Song, Op. 68, No. 4	GS P	Album for the Young, Op. 68
		GS	Introduction to Piano Classics, Vol. II (Mirovitch)
		GS	Selected Piano Solos by Romantic Composers, Bk. II
	Roaming in the Morning, Op. 68, No. 17	GS P	Album for the Young, Op. 68
		GS	Master Series for the Young
	Roundelay, Op. 68, No. 22	GS P	Album for the Young, Op. 68
	Sailor's Song, Op. 68, No. 37		
	Scheherazade, Op. 68, No. 32		
	Solitary Flowers, Op. 82, No. 2	GS AMP	Forest Scenes, Op. 82
		K	Complete Works, Vol. V
		H	Easiest Original Pieces
	Sonata for the Young, Op. 118, No. 1	GS	Three Sonatas for the Young People, Op. 118
	Allegro	K	Complete Works, Vol. VI
	Theme and Variations		
	Doll's Cradle Song		
	Rondoletto		

Composer	Title	Publisher	Volume or Collection
SCHUMANN, R. (Cont.)	Song in Canon Form, Op. 68, No. 27	GS P	Album for the Young, Op. 68
	Spring Song, Op. 68, No. 15		
	Strange Man, Op. 68, No. 29	GS P	Album for the Young, Op. 68
		GS	Selected Piano Solos by Romantic Composers, Bk. II
	Vintage Time, Op. 68, No. 33	GS P	Album for the Young, Op. 68
	Waltz, Op. 124, No. 4	GS K H A PP B Su	Album Leaves, Op. 124 Complete Works, Vol. VI Easiest Original Pieces Beringer's School of Easy Classics: Schumann Hundred Best Short Classics, Bk. II Hours with the Masters, Bk. III Recital Repertoire, Bk. I (Podolsky)
	Winter-Time I, Op. 68, No. 38	GS P	Album for the Young, Op. 68
	Winter-Time II, Op. 68, No. 39		
TSCHAIKOWSKY, P. (1840-1893)	A Song of Sadness, Op. 40, No. 2	GS	Master Series for the Young
	April-Snowdrop, Op. 37a, No. 4	GS PP GS	The Seasons, Op. 37a Hundred Best Short Classics, Bk. III Introduction to Piano Classics, Vol. II
	Chanson Triste	PP	Hundred Best Short Classics, Bk. V
	German Song, Op. 39, No. 17	GS GS	Album for the Young, Op. 39 Master Series for the Young
	January - By the Hearth, Op. 37a, No. 1	GS	The Seasons, Op. 37a
	May - Starlit Night, Op. 37a, No. 5		
	Neapolitan Song, Op. 39, No. 18	GS GS GS	Album for the Young, Op. 39 Master Series for the Young Selected Piano Solos by Romantic Composers, Bk. I
	October - Autumn Song, Op. 37a, No. 10	GS	The Seasons, Op. 37a
	Polka, Op. 39, No. 14	GS GS	Album for the Young, Op. 39 Master Series for the Young
	Russian Dance, Op. 39, No. 13	GS GS	Album for the Young, Op. 39 Master Series for the Young
	Song Without Words, Op. 40, No. 6	GS	Master Series for the Young
	The Hobby Horse, Op. 39, No. 3	GS	Album for the Young, Op. 39

Composer	Title	Publisher	Volume or Collection
TSCHAIKOWSKY, P. (Cont.)	The Nurse's Tale, Op. 39, No. 19		
	The Witch, Op. 39, No. 20	GS	Album for the Young, Op. 39
		He	A Treasury of Easy Classics (Abrams)
	Waltz, Op. 39, No. 8	GS	Album for the Young, Op. 39
			Master Series for the Young
		He	A Treasury of Easy Classics (Abrams)
	Winter Morning, Op. 39, No. 2	GS	Album for the Young, Op. 39
		GS	Master Series for the Young
WEBER, C. (1786-1826)	Andante with Variations, Op. 3, No. 4	GS	Master Series for the Young
	Andantino, Op. 10, No. 2	GS	Master Series for the Young
	Minuet, Op. 3, No. 3	GS	Master Series for the Young
	Moderato (From Sonatina, Op. 3, No. 1)	He	Little Treasury of Sonatinas, Bk. II
		GS	Master Series for the Young
	Theme (From Invitation to the Dance, Op. 65)	GS	Master Series for the Young
	Waltz in A	GS	Master Series for the Young
	Waltz in C		

MUSIC OF THE TWENTIETH CENTURY

Composer	Title	Publisher	Volume or Collection
BARTÓK, BÉLA (1881-1945)	Bagatelles Nos. 1, 3, 4, 6	BH	Fourteen Bagatelles, Op.6
	Bear Dance	K	Ten Easy Pieces for Piano
	Dirge, Op. 8b, No. 1	BH	Four Dirges, Op. 8b
	From "Mikrokosmos"	BH	Mikrokosmos

	Vol. IV
	  Variations on a Folktune
	  Melody		

	Vol. V
	  Boating
	  Peasant Dance
	  A Village Joke
	  Merry Andrew		

	Rumanian Folk Dances Nos. 1, 2, 3, 4	BH	Rumanian Folk Dances
BARVINSKY (1888-)	A Light Ram	L	Children's Piano Pieces by Soviet Composers
BLOCH ERNEST (1880-)	Chanty (From "Poems of the Sea"	GS	51 Piano Pieces from the Modern Repertoire

BRIDGE, FRANK (1844-1924)	From "Miniature Pastorals"
	  4. Allegro giusto
	  5. Andante con moto
	  6. Allegro ma non troppo
		BH	Miniature Pastorals for Piano: 2nd set

CARVAJAL, ARMADO (?)	March	MMC	Meet Modern Music, Pt. II

CASELLA, ALFREDO (1883-1947)	Children's Pieces
	  1. Preludio
	  2. Canon
	  3. Valse Diatonique
	  4. Bolero
	  5. In Honor of Clementi
	  6. Siciliano
	  7. Giga
	  8. Minuetto
	  9. Carillon
	  10. Berceuse
	  11. Galop Final
		AMP	Eleven Children's Pieces

CATURLA, ALEJANDRO (1906-1940)	Piece in Cuban Style, in F Minor	CF	Masters of Our Day

Composer	Title	Publisher	Volume or Collection
COOLS, EUGENE (1877-1936)	From "Our Daughter's Party," Op. 93 2. The Doll's Funeral 3. A Marvelous Story 4. Boys Are Noisy 5. The Rocking Chair	E	Our Daughter's Party, Op. 93
COPLAND, AARON (1900-)	The Young Pioneers	CF	Masters of Our Day
COWELL, HENRY (1897-)	The Harper-Minstrel Sings	CF	Masters of Our Day
FREED, ISADORE (1900-)	A Lake Song	CF	Masters of Our Day
FULEIHAN, ANIS (1900-)	Short Pieces 1. Casual Walk 2. Showing Off	So	Five Very Short Pieces for Talented Young Bipeds
	The Bailiff's Daughter	CF	Published Separately
GLIÉRE, REINHOLD (1875-1926)	In the Fields, Op. 34, No. 7 (From "Characteristic Pieces for Young People")	W	Modern Russian Piano Music
	Mazurka	SG	Russian Piano Classics (Tapper)
	Serenade, Op. 34, No. 19	W	Modern Russian Piano Music
GOEDICKE, ALEXANDER (1877-)	Elegy, Op. 8, No. 2	Su	Recital Repertoire, Bk. II (Podolsky)
	Petrushka	SG	Russian Piano Classics (Tapper)
GOOSSENS, EUGENE (1893-)	"Kaleidoscope," Op. 18 3. Hurdy Gurdy Man 8. The Old Music Box 9. The Clock Work Dancer 10. Lament for Departed Doll 11. A Merry Party	C	Kaleidoscope, Op. 18
GOULD, MORTON (1913-)	Corn-Cob (From "Americano")	CF	Published Separately
GRANADOS, ENRIQUE (1867-1916)	The Last Pavane	MMC	Meet Modern Music, Pt. II
	Theme and Two Variations		
GRETCHANINOFF, ALEXANDER (1864-)	Largo	Sch	The New Piano Book, Vol. II
GROVLEZ, GABRIEL (1879-1944)	From "A Child's Garden" 4. Chanson D'Ancêtre 5. Chanson Pour Faire Danser En Ronds Les Petits Enfants	C	A Child's Garden

Composer	Title	Publisher	Volume or Collection

HARRIS, ROY
(1898-   )
	Little Suite
	  1. Bells
	  2. Sad News
	  3. Children At Play
	  4. Slumber
		GS
		GS
			Little Suite
			51 Piano Pieces from the Modern
			    Repertoire

IBERT, JACQUES (1890-)	La Meneuse de tortues d'or, No. 1 Le palais abandonné, No. 6 Le vieux mendiant, No. 3	Le	Histoires

KABALEVSKY,
  DMITRI
(1904-   )
	Variations, Op. 40, No. 1 in D
	
	Variations, Op. 40, No. 2,
	  in A Minor
		L	Variations, Op. 40

KHACHATURIAN,
  ARAM
(1903-   )
	From "Adventures of Ivan"
	  4. Ivan Goes to A Party
	  5. Ivan Is Very Busy
	  6. Ivan and Natasha
	  7. Ivan's Hobby Horse
	  8. A Tale of Strange Lands
		L	Adventures of Ivan

MENOTTI,
  GIAN-CARLO
(1911-   )
	From "Poemetti"
	  6. The Brook
	  7. The Shepherd
	  8. Nocturne
	  9. The Stranger's Dance
	10. Winter Wind
		R	Poemetti

MIASKOWSKY,
  NIKOLAI
(1881-1951)
	Elegiac Mood
	
	The Hunter's Call
	
	In Ancient Style, Op. 43, No.4
		L
		
		W
			Children's Piano Pieces by Soviet
			    Composers
			
			Modern Russian Piano Music

MILHAUD, DARIUS
(1892-   )
	Suite of 15 Pieces
	
	Two Pieces from "The
	  Child Loves"
	  4. Mother
	  5. Life
	
	Une Journée (One Day)
	  1. Dawn
	  2. Morning
	  3. Noon
	  4. Afternoon
	  5. Twilight
		EV
		
		L
		
		MMC
			The Household Muse
			
			The Child Loves
			
			Une Journée

MOORE, DOUGLAS
(1893-   )
	From "Suite for Piano"
	  1. Air
	  3. Barn Dance
		CF	Suite for Piano

PALMGREN, SELIM (1878-)	Roundelay, Op. 79, No.4 White Lilies	CF SG	Published Separately Published Separately

Composer	Title	Publisher	Volume or Collection
PATTISON, LEE (1890-)	Punchinello	Su	Published Separately
PAZ, JUAN C. (1897-)	At the Coast of Parana	CF	Masters of Our Day
PINTO, OCTAVIO (1890-1950)	From "Memories of Childhood" 3. March Little Soldier 4. Sleeping Time	GS	Memories of Childhood
PISK, PAUL A. (1893-)	From the Ozarks	CF	Masters of Our Day
POLDINI, EDVARD (1869-)	Burletta, Op. 52, No. 1	GS	Published Separately
POULENC, FRANCIS (1889-)	Valse, in C	AMP	Published Separately
RAKOFF, NICOLAS (1908-)	Novelette	W	Modern Russian Piano Music
REBIKOV, VLADIMIR (1866-1920)	The Fairy	GS	Silhouettes, Op. 31
	The Mother By the Cradle		
	Witches Dance	Sch	Piano Album No. II
REGER, MAX (1873-1916)	From "Jugend - Album II" 1. Bange Frage 2. Fast zu keck 3. Erster Streit 4. Was die Gross- mutter erzählt 5. A la Gigue 6. Nordischer Tänz 7. Versöhnung	Sch	Jugend - Album II
RHENE-BATON (1879-1940)	From "Album Rose" 1. Petite Mélodie 2. Bluette 3. Intermezzo 4. Petit Choral 5. Vieille Romance 6. Musette	E	Album Rose
ROLDÁN, AMADEO (1900-)	The "Diablite" Dances	CF	Masters of Our Day
ROZSA, MIKLOS (1907-)	Berceuse from "Kaleidoscope", Op. 19	AMP	Published Separately
	Chinese Carillon, from "Kaleidoscope", Op. 19	AMP	Published Separately
	March, from "Kaleidoscope", Op. 19		

Composer	Title	Publisher	Volume or Collection
SAMINSKY, LAZARE (1882-)	Fooling with Scottie, Op. 45, No. 6	CF	Masters of Our Day
	Mischief, Op. 45, No. 5		
SANJUAN, PEDRO (1886-)	Reflections of Susanne	CF	Masters of Our Day
SATIE, ERIK (1866-1925)	Gymnopedie No. I	S	Published Separately
		M	Published Separately
	Gymnopedie No. II	S	Published Separately
		M	Published Separately
		GS	51 Piano Pieces from the Modern Repertoire
	Gymnopedie No. III	S	Published Separately
		M	Published Separately
	Gnossienne No. 1	He	Published Separately
	Reverie	S	Les Chefs D'Oeuvre des Grands Maitres Contemporains
SCHMITT, FLORENT (1870-)	Bercement, from "Petite Musiques," Op. 32	S	Les Chefs-D'Oeuvre des Grands Maitres Contemporains
	Rocking	CF	Masters of Our Day
	Ronde, from "Petite Musiques"	S	Les Chefs-D'Oeuvre des Grands Maitres Contemporains
	Waltzing	CF	Masters of Our Day
SCOTT, CYRIL (1879-)	A Ballad Told At Candlelight	Sch	Miniatures
		Sch	The New Piano Book, Vol. II
	To An Old Miniature	Sch	Miniatures
SESSIONS, ROGER (1896-)	March	CF	Masters of Our Day
	Scherzino	CF	Masters of Our Day
SÉVÉRAC, D. de (1873-1921)	En Vacances - Series I Invocation to Schumann Grandma's Caresses The Little Girls from Next Door In Chapel In Powdered Wig and Hoop Skirt Games in the Park	E	En Vacances - Series I
SHEBALIN, V. (1902-)	Meditation, Op. 12, No. 3	W	Modern Russian Piano Music
SHEPHERD, ARTHUR (1880-)	The Gay Promenade	CF	Masters of Our Day

Composer	Title	Publisher	Volume or Collection
SIBELIUS, JEAN (1865-)	Evening Calm, Op. 46, No.2	BMC	From The Land of Thousand Lakes
	Olden Days, Op. 46, No. 4		
	Pastorale, Op. 46, No. 5		
	Solitude, Op. 50, No. 3		
SIEGMEISTER, ELIE (1909-)	From "The Children's Day" 3. Playing Clown 4. On A Golden Afternoon 5. Catching Butterflies 6. Bedtime Story	L	The Children's Day
SLAVENSKI, JOSIP (1865-1930)	Slawischer Tanz	Sch	The New Piano Book, Vol. III
STARER, ROBERT (1924-)	Seven Vignettes 1. Fanfare 2. Song Without Words 3. Jig-Saw 4. The Interrupted Waltz 5. Chorale 6. The Camel and the Moon 7. Toccata	L	Seven Vignettes
TANSMAN, ALEXANDRE (1897-)	From "Petite Suite" 2. Berceuse 4. Petite chanson polonaise 6. Caprice	AMP	Petite Suite
	Hide and Seek	AMP	Pour les Enfants, Set IV
	Marche Militaire		
	Music of Bali		
	Procession	De	Piano Miniatures
	Toccata	AMP	Ten Diversions for the Young Pianist
TAYLOR, DEEMS (1885-)	The Smugglers	CF	Masters of Our Day
TCHÉREPNINE, ALEXANDRE (1899-)	From "Pour petits et grands" Set I 2. Le Farceur 3. La Mélodieuse 4. Les Contrastes 6. La Babillarde Set II 1. L'Affligée 2. L'Ibérienne 4. La Dévouée	D	Pour petits et grands
	The Hour of Death	L	Expressions, Op. 81

Composer	Title	Publisher	Volume or Collection

THOMSON, VIRGIL
(1896-   )
	Piano Sonata, No. 4
	  Allegro
	  Adagio
	  Vivace
		EV	Piano Sonata, No. 4

TOCH, ERNST
(1887-   )
	From "Echos of a Small
	  Town"
	  3. Oh, If I Only Had. . . .!
	  4. On the Way to School
	  5. The Hand-Organ Man
	  7. Poor Child
	  9. Full of Fun
	  10. Lonesome
	  11. Following the Band
	  12. Downtown
	  14. Vacation
		AMP	Echos of a Small Town

VILLA-LOBOS,
HEITOR
(1887-   )
	Five Pieces
	  1. The Child's Dream
	  2. The Hunchback
	  3. The Crab
	  4. The Little Dove
	  5. Let Us Go Over the
	     Mountain, O Calunga
		MP	Five Pieces on Popular Children's
			Folktunes of Brazil, Album VI

	Francette et Piá 6. Piá Went to War	E	Published Separately

	From "Guia prático, "
	Album VIII
	  1. Oh, Lemon
	  2. Goodness
	  3. Poor Blind Woman
	  4. Father Francisco
	  5. Fly! Little Bird
	  6. Farmer's Daughters
	  7. Little White Dress
		VL	Guia práctico-Album VIII

	Album IX
	  3. Circle Dance
	  5. Constant
		VL	Guia prático, Album IX

WAXMAN, FRANZ
(1906-   )
	From "The Charm Bracelet"
	  3. The Little Soldier
	  4. The Golden Heart
	  5. The Pony
		L	The Charm Bracelet

SECTION IV

LOWER ADVANCED

GRADES VII AND VIII

MUSIC OF THE SIXTEENTH, SEVENTEENTH AND EIGHTEENTH CENTURIES

Composer	Title	Publisher	Volume or Collection
ARNE, T. A. (1710-1778)	Allegretto in D Minor	A	Beringer's School of Easy Classics: Old English and French Masters
	Allegro (From Sonata in A)	CF B	Classic Sonatas (Podolsky) Hours with the Masters, Bk. V

	Sonata in A
	  Allegro
	  Allegretto
	  Allegro
		CF	Classic Sonatas

BACH, C. P. E. (1714-1788)	Allegro in A	P	Sonaten und Stücke
	Allegro in C		
	Allegro in E		
	Allegro in G		
	Allegro in G	Sch C	Die Söhne Bach Eighteenth Century Music, Vol. II (No. 1)
	Capriccio in D Minor	Sch GS	Die Söhne Bach Introduction to Piano Classics, Vol. II (Mirovitch)
	La Stahl	P	Sonaten und Stücke
	Presto in C Minor	Sch U GS	Die Söhne Bach Old Masters for Young Pianists (Kuranda) Introduction to Piano Classics, Vol. II
	Rondo in B Minor	AS	Published Separately

	Sonata in A
	  Poco allegro
	  Andante lusingando
	  Allegro
		Sch	Six Sonatas, Vol. I (No. 3)

	Sonata in C Minor
	  Allegretto
	  Molto adagio
	  Allegro ma non tanto
		P	Sonaten und Stücke

	Sonata in D Minor
	  Allegro
	  Adagio sostenuto
	  Presto
		Sch	Six Sonatas, Vol. I (No. 2)

	Sonata in G Minor
	  Andante con amoroso
	  Allegretto
	  Allegro moderato
		P	Sonaten und Stücke

	Sonatina nuova in G	Sch	Die Söhne Bach
	Tempo di Minuetto	P	Sonaten und Stücke
	Twelve Variations auf die Folie d'Espagne		

Composer	Title	Publisher	Volume or Collection
BACH, J. C. (1735-1782)	Gavotte in C Minor (From Sonata 5, No. 6)	H GS P	The Sons of Johann Sebastian Bach Introduction to Piano Classics, Vol. II (Mirovitch) Joh. Chr. Bach Sonatas, Bk. II
	Sonata in A, Op. XVII, No. 5 Allegro Presto	P	Joh. Chr. Bach Sonatas, Bk. I
	Sonata in C Minor, Op. XVII, No. 2 Allegro Andante Prestissimo		
	Sonata in D, Op. V, No. 2 Allegro di molto Andante di molto Minuetto		
	Sonata in E, Op. V, No. 5 Allegro Andante Allegro	Sch P	Die Söhne Bach Joh. Chr. Bach Sonatas, Bk. II
	Sonata in E-flat, Op. V, No. 4 Allegro Rondo	P	Joh. Chr. Bach Sonatas, Bk. II
	Sonata in G, Op. XVII, No. 4 Allegro Presto assai	P	Joh. Chr. Bach Sonatas, Bk. I
	Sonata in G, Op. V, No. 3 Allegro Allegretto		
	Theme and Variations, Op. V, No. 3	H P	The Sons of Johann Sebastian Bach Joh. Chr. Bach Sonatas, Bk. II
BACH, J. C. F. (1732-1795)	Allegretto (From Sonata in D)	Sch	Die Söhne Bach
	Andante (From Sonata in D)		
	Rondo (From Sonata in A)	H	The Sons of Johann Sebastian Bach
BACH, J. S. (1685-1750)	Air in E-flat (From French Suite in E-flat, No. IV)	K P GS	French Suites
	Air in E Minor (From Partita in E Minor, No. VI)	K P GS BMC	Partitas Bach for Early Grades, Bk. III
	Bourrée in A Minor (From English Suite in A Minor, No. II)	K P GS BMC PP MM	English Suites Bach for Early Grades, Bk. II Hundred Best Short Classics, Bk. III Your Bach Book (Maier)

Composer	Title	Publisher	Volume or Collection
BACH, J. S. (cont.)	Bourrée in E-flat	K	French Suites (pg. 64)
	Bourrée in F	Sch	Little Bach Book (No. 5)
	Courante in A	B	Hours with the Masters, Bk. II
		Sch	Little Piano Book of Wilhelm Friedemann (No. 12)
	Courante in E (From French Suite in E, No. VI)	K P GS	French Suites
	Courante in G (From Partita in G, No. V)	K P GS	Partitas
		BMC	Bach for Early Grades, Bk. III
	Duet in E Minor	P K	Four Duets (No. 1)
		CF	Road to Piano Artistry, Vol. IX (Scionti)
	Entrée in F	Sch	Little Bach Book (No. 2)
	Fuga in E-flat	K	Various Short Preludes and Fugues (pg. 48)
	Fughetta in D Minor	GS	Eighteen Little Preludes and Fugues (No. 6)
		K	Various Short Preludes and Fugues (pg. 41)
		GS	Short Preludes and Fugues (pg. 27)
		P	Short Preludes and Fugues (pg. 36)
	Fughetta in E Minor	K	Various Short Preludes and Fugues (pg. 43)
		GS	Short Preludes and Fugues (pg. 29)
		P	Short Preludes and Fugues (pg. 40)
		GS	Eighteen Little Preludes and Fugues (No. 16)
	Fughetta in G	GS	Eighteen Little Preludes and Fugues (No. 3)
	Fugue in C	K	Various Short Preludes and Fugues (Pg. 24)
		GS	Short Preludes and Fugues (pg. 22)
		P	Short Preludes and Fugues (pg. 30)
		GS	Eighteen Little Preludes and Fugues (No. 5)
	Fugue in C	K	Various Short Preludes and Fugues (pg. 26)
		GS	Short Preludes and Fugues (pg. 24)
		P	Short Preludes and Fugues (pg. 32)
		GS	Eighteen Little Preludes and Fugues (No. 13)
	Fugue in C Minor	K	Various Short Preludes and Fugues (pg. 22)
		GS	Eighteen Little Preludes and Fugues (No. 4)
		GS	Short Preludes and Fugues (pg. 20)
		P	Short Preludes and Fugues (Pg. 28)

Composer	Title	Publisher	Volume or Collection
BACH, J. S. (cont.)	Fugue in E Minor	K P GS	Well Tempered Clavier, Bk. I
		BMC	Bach for Early Grades, Bk. III
	Fugue in G	K P GS	Well Tempered Clavier, Bk. II
	Gavottes I and II (From English Suite in D Minor, No. VI)	K P GS	English Suites
	Gavottes I and II (From French Suite in E, No. VI)	K P GS	French Suites
	Gigue in A	Sch MM	Little Piano Book of Wilhelm Friedemann Your Bach Book (Maier)
	Gigue in B-flat (From Partita in B-flat, No. I)	K P GS	Partitas
		GS	Bach Album (Heinze)
		PP	Hundred Best Short Classics, Bk. IV
	Inventions - Two Part	K P GS	Two Part Inventions
	2. C Minor 3. D Major 5. E-flat Major 6. E Major 10. G Major 11. G Minor 12. A Major	MM	Your Bach Book (Maier)
	14. B-flat Major	MM PP	Your Bach Book (Maier) Hundred Best Short Classics, Bk. II
	15. B Minor	MM	Your Bach Book (Maier)
	Inventions - Three Part	K P GS	Three Part Inventions
	1. C Major 2. C Minor 4. D Minor 5. E-flat Major		
	6. E Major	CF	Road to Piano Artistry, Vol. IX (Scionti)
	10. G Major		
	11. G Minor	CF	Road to Piano Artistry, Vol. VIII (Scionti)
	13. A Minor 15. B Minor		
	Little Prelude in A Minor	K	Various Short Preludes and Fugues (No. 12)
		GS	Eighteen Little Preludes and Fugues (No. 18)
		K	First Bach Book (No. 25)
		Sch	Little Bach Book (pg. 8)
		GS	Short Preludes and Fugues (No. 12)

Composer	Title	Publisher	Volume or Collection
BACH, J. S. (cont.)	Little Prelude in D	K	Various Short Preludes and Fugues (pg. 8)
		GS	Short Preludes and Fugues (No. 4 of 12 Little)
		GS	Eighteen Little Preludes and Fugues (No. 13, Key of C)
		Sch	Little Piano Book of Wilhelm Friedemann (No. 15)
	Little Prelude in D	K	Various Short Preludes and Fugues (pg. 19)
		P	Short Preludes and Fugues, (pg. 22)
		GS	Eighteen Little Preludes and Fugues (No. 1)
		GS	Short Preludes and Fugues (pg. 17)
		PP	Hundred Best Short Classics, Bk. III
		CF	Road to Piano Artistry, Vol. VI (Scionti)
	Little Prelude in E	K	Various Short Preludes and Fugues (pg. 20)
		GS	Short Preludes and Fugues (pg. 18)
		U	Old Masters for Young Pianists (Kuranda)
		P	Short Preludes and Fugues (pg. 24)
	Little Prelude in E Minor	K	Various Short Preludes and Fugues (pg. 21)
		GS	Short Preludes and Fugues (pg. 19)
		P	Short Preludes and Fugues (pg. 26)
	Little Prelude in E Minor	K	Various Short Preludes and Fugues (pg. 42)
		GS	Short Preludes and Fugues (pg. 28)
		P	Short Preludes and Fugues (pg. 38)
	Little Prelude in F	K	Various Short Preludes and Fugues (pg. 12)
		GS	Short Preludes and Fugues (pg. 10)
		P	Short Preludes and Fugues (pg. 12)
		Sch	Little Piano Book of Wilhelm Friedemann (No. 16)
	Little Prelude in F	GS	Eighteen Little Preludes and Fugues (No. 7)
	Little Prelude in G Minor	K	Various Short Preludes and Fugues (pg. 14)
		GS	Short Preludes and Fugues (pg. 12)
		P	Short Preludes and Fugues (pg. 14)
		K	First Bach Book (No. 24)
		Sch	Little Piano Book of Wilhelm Friedemann (No. 14)
	Little Prelude in G	GS	Eighteen Little Preludes and Fugues (No. 3)
	Minuet in B Minor, (From French Suite in B Minor, No. III)	K	French Suites
		P	
		GS	
		GS	Bach Album (Heinze)
		BMC	Bach for Early Grades, Bk. III
		B	Hours with the Masters, Bk. III

Composer	Title	Publisher	Volume or Collection
BACH, J. S. (cont.)	Minuet in B-flat, (From Partita in B-flat, No. I)	K P GS GS	Partitas Bach Album (Heinze)
	Minuets I and II in D Minor (From French Suite in D Minor No. I)	K P GS	French Suites
	Minuet in E-flat (From French Suite in E-flat No. IV)	K P GS	French Suites
	Minuets I and II in F (From English Suite in F No. IV)	K P GS	English Suites
	Passepieds I and II (From English Suite in E Minor No. V)	K P GS GS	English Suites Bach Album (Heinze)
	Polonaise in E (From French Suite in E No. VI)	K P GS GS BMC CF B U	French Suites Master Series for the Young Bach for Early Grades, Bk. III Road to Piano Artistry, Vol. V (Scionti) Hours with the Masters, Bk. IV Old Masters for Young Pianists (Kuranda)
	Prelude in A-flat	K P GS	Well Tempered Clavier, Vol. I (No. 17)
	Prelude in A Minor		(No. 22)
	Prelude in B-flat		(No. 21)
	Prelude in B		(No. 23)
	Prelude in B Minor	K P GS	Well Tempered Clavier, Vol. II (No. 24)
	Prelude in D Minor	K P GS	Well Tempered Clavier, Vol. I (No. 6)
	Prelude in E-flat	K P GS	Well Tempered Clavier, Vol. II (No. 7)
	Prelude in F Minor		(No. 12)
	Prelude in F Minor	GS CF Sch	First Lessons in Bach, Bk. II (Carroll) Bach First Lessons, Bk. II (Carroll) Little Bach Book
	Prelude in G	K P GS	Well Tempered Clavier, Vol. I (No. 15)
	Prelude in G	K P GS	Well Tempered Clavier, Vol. II (No. 15)

Composer	Title	Publisher	Volume or Collection
BACH, J. S. (cont.)	Sarabande in A Minor (From English Suite in A Minor No. II)	K P GS MM	English Suites Your Bach Book (Maier)
	Sarabande in D Minor (From French Suite in D Minor No. I)	K P GS GS B	French Suites Bach Album (Heinze) Hours with the Masters, Bk. V
	Sarabande in E-flat (From French Suite in E-flat No. IV)	K P GS	French Suites
	Sarabande in E Minor (From English Suite in E Minor No. V)	K P GS GS GS CF PP	English Suites Bach Album (Heinze) First Lessons in Bach, Bk. II (Carroll) Bach First Lessons, Bk. II (Carroll) Hundred Best Classics, Bk. III
	Sarabande in F (From English Suite in F No. IV)	K P GS	English Suites
	Sarabande in F Minor	Sch	Little Bach Book
	Sarabande in G Minor (From English Suite in G Minor No. III)	K P GS	English Suites
	Scherzo in A Minor (From Partita in A Minor)	K P GS CF	Partitas Bach First Lessons, Bk. II
	Solo per il Cembalo	K P	Little Notebook of Anna Magdalena Bach Notenbuch der Anna Magdalena Bach
BACH, W. F. (1710-1784)	Fuga in B-flat (Fughetta)	P GS	Fugues and Polonaises (No. 7) Eighteen Little Preludes and Fugues (No. 5)
	Fuga in D (Fughetta)	P Sch GS	Fugues and Polonaises (No. 3) Die Söhne Bach Eighteen Little Preludes and Fugues (No. 1)
	Fuga in D Minor (Fughetta)	P GS	Fugues and Polonaises (No. 4) Eighteen Little Preludes and Fugues (No. 2)
	Lamento in E Minor (Sarabande from Sonata in G)	Sch GS H	Die Söhne Bach Introduction to Piano Classics, Vol. II (Mirovitch) The Sons of Johann Sebastian Bach
	Polonaise in C Minor	P H	Fugues and Polonaises (No. 2) The Sons of Johann Sebastian Bach

Composer	Title	Publisher	Volume or Collection
BACH, W. F. (cont.)	Polonaise in D Minor	P	Fugues and Polonaises (No. 4)
		Sch	Die Söhne Bach
	Polonaise in F	P	Fugues and Polonaises (No. 9)
		Sch	Die Söhne Bach
BLOW, J. (1649-1708)	Courante and Fugue in C	GS	Early Keyboard Music, Vol. I
		A	Beringer's School of Easy Classics: Old English and French Masters
	Prelude in C	GS	Early Keyboard Music, Vol. I
BÖHM, G. (1661-1733)	Presto in G Minor	K	Old Masters of the 16th, 17th and 18th Centuries
BULL, J. (1563-1628)	Courante, Jewell	GS	Early Keyboard Music, Vol. I
	Galiardo II in D Minor		
BYRD, W. (1542-1623)	Galiardo in G Minor	GS	Early Keyboard Music, Vol. I
	Sellenger's Round		
	The Carman's Whistle		
	Victoria		
CIMAROSA, D. (1749-1801)	Sonatas: Nos. 1, 3, 4, 6, 7, 8, 10	E	Thirty Two Sonatas, Vol. I
	Sonatas: Nos. 11, 12, 14, 18, 19, 20		Thirty Two Sonatas, Vol. II
	Sonatas: (12 Sonatas) Complete		Thirty Two Sonatas, Vol. III
CORELLI, A. (1653-1713)	Giga	PP	Hundred Best Short Classics, Bk. IV
COUPERIN, F. (1668-1733)	Gavotte in G Minor	BH	Airs and Dances, Bk. II (Dorolle)
	La Bandoline - Rondeau	GS	Early Keyboard Music, Vol. II
	Les Petits Moulins à Vent	K	Old Masters of the 16th, 17th and 18th Centuries
		He	A Treasury of Easy Classics (Abrams)
		GS	Early Keyboard Music, Vol. II
		A	Beringer's School of Easy Classics: Old English and French Masters
		GS	Published Separately
	Rigaudon in D Minor	K	Old Masters of the 16th, 17th and 18th Centuries
	Rondeau	K	Little Notebook of Anna Magdalena Bach
	Soeuer Monique	GS	Early Keyboard Music, Vol. II
		GS	Published Separately
		PP	Hundred Best Short Classics, Bk. V
	Chaconne in D Minor	GS	Early Keyboard Music, Vol. I

Composer	Title	Publisher	Volume or Collection
DAQUIN (1694-1772)	Le Coucou	K	Old Masters of the 16th, 17th and 18th Centuries
		B	Hours with the Masters, Bk. V
		PP	Hundred Best Short Classics, Bk. III
FISCHER, J. K. F. (1650-1746)	Fugue in G	K	A Little Book of Fugues (No. 10)
	Prelude (From Second Suite)	K	Old Masters of the 16th, 17th and 18th Centuries
	Rondeau (From Second Suite)		
	Sarabande in D Minor		
GALUPPI, B. (1706-1785)	Adagio (From Sonata in D)	K	Old Masters of the 16th, 17th and 18th Centuries
		CF	Classic Sonatas (Podolsky)
		OD	Early Italian Piano Music
	Vivace in C Minor	HC	Clavecinistes Italiens
GIBBONS, O. (1583-1675)	The Queen's Command	GS	Early Keyboard Music, Vol. I
GRAUN, C. H. (1701-1759)	Gigue in B-flat Minor	K	Old Masters of the 16th, 17th and 18th Centuries
GRAZIOLI, G. (1770-1820)	Sonata in G Moderato Adagio Tempo di Minuetto	CF	Published Separately
	Singing to the Lute (From Sonata in G)	SG	Classics from the 17th and 18th Centuries
	Minuetto in G (From Sonata in G)	OD	Early Italian Piano Music
HANDEL, G. F. (1685-1759)	Air in G (From Suite XIV)	K	Suites and Chaconnes, Vol. II
		P	Handel Suites, Vol. II
		GS	Master Series for the Young
		GS	Twelve Easy Pieces
		He	A Little Treasury of Classics, Bk. IV
	(Allegro)	U	Old Masters for Young Pianists (Kuranda)
	Air and Variations in B-flat	K	Suites and Chaconnes, Vol. II
	Air and Variations in E (From Suite V) (Harmonious Blacksmith)	K	Suites and Chaconnes, Vol. I
		P	Suites, Vol. I
		PP	Hundred Best Short Classics, Bk. IV
		GS	Master Series for the Young
	Air and Variations in F	Sch	Aylesford Pieces No. 16
		Sch	Pieces for Harpsichord, Vol. II (No. 53)
	Allegro in D Minor (From Suite X)	K	Suites and Chaconnes, Vol. II
		P	Suites, Vol. II
	Allegro in D Minor	Sch	Aylesford Pieces (No. 11)
		Sch	Pieces for Harpsichord, Vol. II (No. 54)
	Allegro I in F (From Suite II)	K	Suites and Chaconnes, Vol. I
		P	Suites, Vol. I

Composer	Title	Publisher	Volume or Collection
HANDEL, G. F. (cont.)	Allegro in G (From Suite XIV)	K P PP	Suites and Chaconnes, Vol. II Suites, Vol. II Hundred Best Short Classics, Bk. V
	Allegro in G Minor (From Suite VII)	K P H	Suites and Chaconnes, Vol. I Suites, Vol. I Easiest Original Pieces
	Allemande in A Minor	Sch Sch	Pieces for Harpsichord, Vol. II (No. 43) Aylesford Pieces (No. 17)
	Allemande in F Minor (From Suite VIII)	K P GS B GS	Suites and Chaconnes, Vol. I Suites, Vol. I Twelve Easy Pieces Hours with the Masters, Bk. V Master Series for the Young
	Allemande in G (From Suite XIV)	K P H	Suites and Chaconnes, Vol. II Suites, Vol. II Easiest Original Pieces (No. 6)
	Allemande in G Minor (From Suite XVI)	P GS GS B	Suites, Vol. II Twelve Easy Pieces Master Series for the Young Hours with the Masters, Bk. V
	Aria in C Minor	Sch	Pieces for Harpsichord, Vol. I (No. 13)
	Aria in C Minor	Sch	Pieces for Harpsichord, Vol. II (No. 52)
	Arpeggio and Gigue in G Minor	Sch	Pieces for Harpsichord, Vol. I (Nos. 19 and 20)
	Capriccio in A Minor	GS	Master Series for the Young
	(Fantasie in A Minor)	PP	Hundred Best Short Classics, Bk. IV
	Chaconne in C	Sch	Pieces for Harpsichord, Vol. I (No. 15)
	Chaconne in G No. 2	K	Suites and Chaconnes, Vol. II
	Chaconne in G, No. 9	K	Suites and Chaconnes, Vol. II
	Chaconne in G Minor	Sch	Pieces for Harpsichord, Vol. II (No. 45)
	Concerto	Sch Sch	Pieces for Harpsichord, Vol. I (No. 33) Aylesford Pieces (No. 7)
	Courante in F Minor (From Suite VIII)	K P	Suites and Chaconnes, Vol. I Suites, Vol. I
	Courante in G (From Suite XIV)	K P H GS	Suites and Chaconnes, Vol. II Suites, Vol. II Easiest Original Pieces Master Series for the Young
	(Corrente)	GS	Twelve Easy Pieces
	Entrée	Sch Sch	Pieces for Harpsichord, Vol. I (No. 2) Aylesford Pieces (No. 2)
	Fantasia in C	H B	Easiest Original Pieces Hours with the Masters, Bk. V
	(Sonata in C)	CF	Classic Sonatas (Podolsky)
	(Sonata in C)	GS	Twelve Easy Pieces
	Fughetta in D (From Six Fughettas)	H	Easiest Original Pieces

Composer	Title	Publisher	Volume or Collection
HANDEL, G. F. (cont.)	Gavotte and Variations in G (From Suite XIV)	P	Suites, Vol. II
		K	Suites and Chaconnes, Vol. II
		GS	Master Series for the Young (Incomplete)
		GS	Twelve Easy Pieces
	Gigue in B-flat (From Suite XIII)	K	Suites and Chaconnes, Vol. II
		P	Suites, Vol. II
		H	Easiest Original Pieces
	Gigue in D Minor (From Suite XI)	K	Suites and Chaconnes, Vol. II
		P	Suites, Vol. II
		GS	Master Series for the Young
		GS	Twelve Easy Pieces
	Gigue in G Major (From Suite XIV)	K	Suites and Chaconnes, Vol. II
		P	Suites, Vol. II
		GS	Master Series for the Young
	Gigue in G Minor (From Suite XVI)	K	Suites and Chaconnes, Vol. II
		P	Suites, Vol. II
		B	Hours with the Masters, Bk. III
	Little Fugue No. 2 in C	GS	Master Series for the Young
	Menuet in A Minor	Sch	Pieces for Harpsichord, Vol. II (No. 68)
	Menuet in D Minor	Sch	Pieces for Harpsichord, Vol. II (No. 55)
	Menuetto in D Minor (From Suite X)	K	Suites and Chaconnes, Vol. II
		P	Suites, Vol. II
	Ouverture in G Minor	Sch	Pieces for Harpsichord, Vol. I (No. 1)
		Sch	Aylesford Pieces (No. 1)
	Passacaglia in G Minor (From Suite VII)	K	Suites and Chaconnes, Vol. I
		P	Suites, Vol. I
		GS	Master Series for the Young
	Prelude in A Minor	Sch	Pieces for Harpsichord, Vol. I (No. 17)
	Prelude in C	Sch	Pieces for Harpsichord, Vol. I (No. 12)
	Prelude in D Minor	Sch	Pieces for Harpsichord, Vol. II (No. 49)
	Prelude in D Minor	Sch	Pieces for Harpsichord, Vol. I (No. 10)
		Sch	Aylesford Pieces (No. 8)
	Sonata in G Minor	Sch	Pieces for Harpsichord, Vol. I (No. 31)
	Sonata in G Minor	Sch	(No. 32)
	Sonatina in A Minor	Sch	Pieces for Harpsichord, Vol. II (No. 44)
		Sch	Aylesford Pieces (No. 20)
	Suite in B-flat, No. XIII Allemande Courante Sarabande Gigue	K	Suites and Chaconnes, Vol. II
		P	Suites, Vol. II
	Suite in D Minor, No. XI Allemande Courante Sarabande Gigue	K	Suites and Chaconnes, Vol. II
		P	Suites, Vol. II

Composer	Title	Publisher	Volume or Collection
HANDEL, G. F. (cont.)	Suite in D Minor, No. XV Allemande Courante Sarabande Gigue	P	Suites, Vol. II
	Suite in E, No. V Prelude Allemande Courante Air and Variations	K P	Suites and Chaconnes, Vol. I Suites, Vol. I
	Suite in E Minor, No. XII Allemande Sarabande Gigue	P	Suites, Vol. II
	Suite in G No. XIV Allemande Allegro Courante Air Menuet Gavotte and Variations	K P	Suites and Chaconnes, Vol. II Suites, Vol. II
	Suite in G Minor, No. VII Ouverture Andante Allegro Sarabande Gigue Passacaille	K P	Suites and Chaconnes, Vol. I Suites, Vol. II
	Suite in G Minor, No. XVI Allemande Courante Sarabande Gigue	P	Suites, Vol. II
HASSE, J. A. (1699-1783)	Adagio in D Minor (From Sonata Op. 7)	GS	Introduction to Piano Classics, Vol. III (Mirovitch)
	Allegro in B-flat	CF GS	Classic Sonatas (Podolsky) Introduction to Piano Classics, Vol. III
	Gigue in D Minor (From Sonata Op. 7)	GS CF	Introduction to Piano Classics, Vol. III Classic Sonatas (Podolsky)
HÄSSLER, J. W. (1747-1822)	Sonata in C (From Six Easy Sonatas), No. I Poco allegro Largo Allegro quasi presto	CF P	Classic Sonatas (Podolsky) Six Easy Sonatas
	Sonata in C (From Six Easy Sonatas), No. II Largo ed espressivo Allegro molto	CF P	Classic Sonatas (Podolsky) Six Easy Sonatas
HAYDN, J. (1732-1809)	Adagio (From Sonata in G)	P K	Haydn Sonatas, Vol. IV (No. 37) Vol. II (No. 31)

Composer	Title	Publisher	Volume or Collection
HAYDN, J. (cont.)		H	Easiest Original Pieces
	Allegro molto (From Sonata in G)	P K	Haydn Sonatas, Vol. IV (No. 37) Vol. II (No. 31)
	Andante (From Sonata in D)	P K GS	Haydn Sonatas, Vol. I (No. 9) Vol. I (No. 9) Vol. I (No. 9)
	Arietta con Variazione in A Major	K A	Haydn: Eight Various Compositions Beringer's School of Easy Classics: Haydn
	Arietta con Variazione in E-flat	K H A	Haydn: Eight Various Compositions Easiest Original Pieces
	Finale: Allegro assai (From Sonata in D)	P K GS	Haydn: Sonatas, Vol. I (No. 9) Vol. I (No. 9) Vol. I (No. 9)
	Finale: Presto (From Sonata in A)	P H	Haydn Sonatas, Vol. III (No. 33) Easiest Original Pieces
	Finale: Presto (From Sonata in D)	P H	Haydn Sonatas, Vol. III (No. 31) Easiest Original Pieces
	Finale: Tempo di Menuetto (From Sonata in E-flat)	P K GS	Haydn Sonatas, Vol. I (No. 3) Vol. I (No. 3) Vol. I (No. 3)
	Finale: Tempo di Menuetto (From Sonata in E)	P K	Haydn Sonatas, Vol. IV (No. 40) Vol. II (No. 34)
	Menuetto (From Sonata in G)	P K	Haydn Sonatas, Vol. IV (No. 37) Vol. II (No. 31)
	Rondo in A	GS	Published Separately
	Sonata in A Allegro Menuetto Presto	P	Haydn Sonatas, Vol. II (No. 23)
	Sonata in A Andante Menuetto Finale	P K	Haydn Sonatas, Vol. III (No. 29) Vol. II (No. 26)
	Sonata in A Allegro Adagio Tempo di Menuetto con variazioni	P K	Vol. IV (No. 36) Vol. II (No. 30)
	Sonata in A-flat Moderato Menuetto Rondo	P	Vol. IV (No. 41)
	Sonata in B-flat Moderato Largo Menuetto	P	Vol. II (No. 22)

Composer	Title	Publisher	Volume or Collection
HAYDN, J. (cont.)	Sonata in C	P	Vol. I (No. 5)
	Allegro con brio	K	Vol. I (No. 5)
	Adagio	GS	Vol. I (No. 5)
	Finale		
	Sonata in D	P	Vol. I (No. 7)
	Allegro con brio	K	Vol. I (No. 7)
	Largo e sostenuto	GS	Vol. I (No. 7)
	Finale		
	Sonata in D	P	Vol. II (No. 20)
	Allegro	K	Vol. I (No. 19)
	Adagio	GS	Vol. II (No. 19)
	Tempo di Menuetto		
	Sonata in E	P	Vol. II (No. 18)
	Moderato	K	Vol. I (No. 17)
	Menuetto	GS	Vol. II (No. 17)
	Finale		
	Sonata in E Minor	P	Vol. I (No. 2)
	Presto	K	Vol. I (No. 2)
	Adagio	GS	Vol. I (No. 2)
	Finale		
	Sonata in F	P	Vol. II (No. 21)
	Allegro moderato	K	Vol. I (No. 20)
	Adagio	GS	Vol. II (No. 20)
	Finale		
	Sonata in F	P	Vol. IV (No. 34)
	Moderato	K	Vol. II (No. 28)
	Larghetto		
	Allegro		
	Sonata in G	P	Vol. II (No. 12)
	Allegro con brio	GS	Vol. II (No. 11)
	Menuetto	K	Vol. II (No. 11)
	Finale	GS	Master Series for the Young
	Sonata in G	P	Vol. II (No. 17)
	Allegro con brio	K	Vol. I (No. 16)
	Adagio	GS	Vol. II (No. 16)
	Prestissimo		
	Tema con Variazioni	K	Eight Various Compositions
		GS	Master Series for the Young
KIRNBERGER, J. (1721-1783)	Gigue in C Minor	K	Old Masters of the 16th, 17th and 18th Centuries
	La Galliarde		
KRIEGER, J. (1649-1725)	Corrente	K	Old Masters of the 16th, 17th and 18th Centuries
	Sarabande with Double		
KUHNAU, J. (1660-1722)	Bourrée in D Minor	K	Old Masters of the 16th, 17th and 18th Centuries
	Gavotte in D	U	Grosse Meister für kleine Hände

Composer	Title	Publisher	Volume or Collection
KUHNAU, J. (cont.)		K	Old Masters of the 16th, 17th and 18th Centuries
	Gigue in C Minor		
	Prelude in B Minor	EV	New Recital Repertoire (Mirovitch)
LOEILLET, J. (1653-1728)	Suite in G Minor	GS Su	Early Keyboard Music, Bk. II Published Separately
	Allemande Courante Sarabande Minuetto Gigue		
LULLY, J. B. (1632-1687)	Courante in E Minor	GS	Early Keyboard Music, Bk. I
	Sarabande in C		
MARPURG, F. W. (1718-1795)	La Badine	K	Old Masters of the 16th, 17th and 18th Centuries
	La Voltigeuse		
MATTHESON, J. (1681-1764)	Air (From C Minor, Suite No. 5) (Aria)	GS BH	Early Keyboard Music, Bk. II Airs and Dances, Bk. II (Dorolle)
	Gigue in E Minor	GS K GS	Early Keyboard Music, Bk. II Old Masters of the 16th, 17th and 18th Centuries Introduction to Piano Classics, Bk. III (Mirovitch)
	Gigue II in G Minor	GS	Early Keyboard Music, Bk. II
	Sarabande mit Drei Variations (From Suite XII)	GS	Early Keyboard Music, Bk. II
MEHUL, E. (1763-1817)	Sonata in A, Op. 1, No. 3	CF	Published Separately (Podolsky)
MOZART, W. A. (1756-1791)	Adagio (From Sonata in F (K 280)	K P	Mozart Sonatas and Three Fantasies
	Ah! Vous Dirai-je Maman (From Variations)	H GS	Easiest Original Pieces Master Series for the Young
	Fantasie in D Minor (K 397)	K GS GS	Mozart Sonatas and Three Fantasies Mozart - Twelve Piano Pieces Mozart Fantasias and Rondos
	Menuetto in D (K 355)	K GS GS	Mozart Piano Pieces Mozart Twelve Piano Pieces Master Series for the Young
	Rondo in D (K 485)	K GS GS H GS	Mozart Piano Pieces Mozart Twelve Piano Pieces Mozart Fantasias and Rondos Easiest Original Pieces Master Series for the Young

Composer	Title	Publisher	Volume or Collection
MOZART, W. A. (cont.)	Rondo in F (K 494)	K	Mozart Piano Pieces

	Sonata in A (K 331)
	   Andante grazioso
	   Menuetto
	   Alla Turca
		K
		P
			Mozart Sonatas

	Sonata in G (K 283)
	   Allegro
	   Andante
	   Presto
		K
		P
			Mozart Sonatas

	Sonatina in A, No. II
	   Allegro
	   Menuetto
	   Adagio
	   Rondo
		Sch
		H
		MMC
			Six Viennese Sonatinas

	Sonatina in B-flat, No. IV
	   Andante grazioso
	   Menuetto
	   Rondo
		Sch
		H
		MMC
			Six Viennese Sonatinas

	Sonatina in C, No. I
	   Allegro brilliante
	   Allegretto
	   Adagio
	   Allegro
		Sch
		H
		MMC
			Six Viennese Sonatinas

	Sonatina in C, No. VI
	   Allegro
	   Menuetto
	   Adagio
	   Finale
		Sch
		H
		MMC
		CF
			Six Viennese Sonatinas
			
			Road to Piano Artistry, Vol. VIII (Scionti)

	Sonatina in D, No. III
	   Andante
	   Menuetto
	   Rondo
		Sch
		H
		MMC
			Six Viennese Sonatinas

MUFFAT, J. T. (1690-1770)	Allegro spiritoso	GS	Early Keyboard Music, Vol. II
	Fantasia in G Minor	GS	Introduction to Piano Classics, Vol. III (Mirovitch)
	Fugues, Nos. 6, 7, 8, 11, 15, 17	K	A Little Book of Fugues
	Menuet in D Minor	K	Old Masters of the 16th, 17th and 18th Centuries

	Partita in C
	   Prelude
	   Fantasie
	   Sarabanda
	   Rigaudon
	   Menuet
	   Paysan
		Sch	Partiten und Stücke

	Partita in C Minor
	   Ouverture
	   Allemande
	   Courante
		Sch	Partiten und Stücke

Composer	Title	Publisher	Volume or Collection
MUFFAT, J. T. (cont.)	Sarabande Gavotte Menuet Gigue		
	Rigaudon in F	K	Old Masters of the 16th, 17th and 18th Centuries
	Suite in B-flat Sarabande La Hardiesse Minuet I Minuet II Air Gigue	GS	Early Keyboard Music, Bk. II
	Zwei kleine Fugen	Sch	Partiten und Stücke
MURCHHAUSER, F. (1663-1738)	Aria Pastoralis Variata	K GS	Old Masters of the 16th, 17th and 18th Centuries Early Keyboard Music, Bk. II
	Fugue in F	K	A Little Book of Fugues (No. 13)
NEEFE, C. G. (1748-1798)	Toccata	GS	Introduction to Piano Classics, Vol. III (Mirovitch)
NICHELMANN, C. (1717-1762)	Gigue in C Minor	K	Old Masters of the 16th, 17th and 18th Centuries
	La Galliarde in C		
	La Tendre		
PACHELBEL, J. (1653-1706)	Ciaconna in D	GS	Early Keyboard Music, Bk. I
	Fugue in C Minor	EV	New Recital Repertoire (Mirovitch)
	Fugue in D Minor	K	A Little Book of Fugues (No. 12)
	Fugue in F	K K EV	(No. 16) Old Masters of the 16th, 17th and 18th Centuries New Recital Repertoire (Mirovitch)
	Fugues on the Magnificat, Nos. 4, 5, 6	K	Old Masters of the 16th, 17th and 18th Centuries
PURCELL, H. (1658-1695)	Prelude in C (From Suite in C, No. V)	GS GS B GS H	Purcell Keyboard Suites Early Keyboard Music, Bk. I Hours with the Masters, Bk. IV Introduction to Piano Classics, Vol. III (Mirovitch) Contemporaries of Purcell
	Suite in A Minor, No. IV Prelude Almand Courante Sarabande	GS GS	Purcell: Keyboard Suites Early Keyboard Music, Bk. I
	Suite in C, No. V Prelude		

Composer	Title	Publisher	Volume or Collection
PURCELL, H. (cont.)	Almand Courante Saraband Cebell (Gavot) Minuet Riggadoon Intrada March		
	Suite in D, No. VI Prelude Almand Hornpipe		
	Suite in D Minor, No. VII Almand Courante Hornpipe		
	Suite in F, No. VIII Prelude Almand Hornpipe Minuet		
RAMEAU, J. P. (1683-1764)	Gigue en Rondeau in E Minor	GS	Early Keyboard Music, Bk. II
	Gigue en Rondeau in E	BH	Airs and Dances, Bk. II (Dorolle)
	Musette en Rondeau	K	Old Masters of the 16th, 17th and 18th Centuries
		A	Beringer's School of Easy Classics: Old English and French Masters
		GS	Early Keyboard Music, Bk. II
	Pavane	Su	Recital Repertoire, Bk. III
	Rigaudon in E, II	GS	Early Keyboard Music, Bk. II
RUTINI, G. M. (1730-1797)	Giga Presto in F Minor	HC	Clavecinistes Italiens
SCARLATTI, A. (1659-1725)	Tema con Variazioni in E-flat (Toccata Settima)	OD	Early Italian Piano Music
SCARLATTI, D. (1685-1757)	Larghetto in F	GS	Early Keyboard Music, Bk. II
	Sonata in A, L. 94	M	Twelve Easy Scarlatti Sonatas (Mirovitch) (No. 8)
	Sonata in A Minor, L. 93		(No. 7)
	Sonata in B Minor, L. 263	CF	Road to Piano Artistry, Vol. VII (Scionti)
		K	Sixty Sonatas
		R	Twenty Five Sonatas
		BMC	Twenty Seven Selected Sonatas
	Sonata in C, (L 358)	M	Twelve Easy Scarlatti Sonatas (Mirovitch) (No. 10)
		GS	Early Keyboard Music, Bk. II

Composer	Title	Publisher	Volume or Collection
SCARLATTI, D. (cont.)	Sonata in D, (L 463)	P	Twenty Five Sonatas
		I	9 Sonatas
		GS	Early Keyboard Music, Bk. II
		PP	Hundred Best Short Classics, Bk. V
		OD	Early Italian Piano Music
		K	Sixty Sonatas
		R	Twenty Five Sonatas
		A	Beringer's School of Easy Classics: Scarlatti
	Sonata in D Minor, (L 58)	M	Twelve Easy Scarlatti Sonatas (Mirovitch) (No. 6)
	Sonata in D Minor, (L 413) (Pastorale)	M	Twelve Easy Scarlatti Sonatas (Mirovitch) (No. 11)
	(Pastorale)	P	Twenty Five Sonatas
	(Pastorale)	GS	Early Keyboard Music, Bk. II
		K	Sixty Sonatas
		PP	Hundred Best Short Classics, Bk. V
		A	Beringer's School of Easy Classics: Scarlatti
	(Pastorale in E Minor)	I	9 Sonatas for Piano
		CF	Road to Piano Artistry, Vol. IV (Scionti)
	Sonata in F, (L 433) (Siciliano)	OD	Early Italian Piano Music
		K	Old Masters
	(Pastorale)	K	Sixty Sonatas (No. 43)
		R	Twenty Five Sonatas (No. 17)
	Sonata in G, (L 84)	M	Twelve Easy Scarlatti Sonatas (Mirovitch) (No. 4)
		A	Beringer's School of Easy Classics: Scarlatti
	Sonata in G, (L 388)	M	Twelve Easy Scarlatti Sonatas (Mirovitch) (No. 9)
		K	Sixty Sonatas (No. 2)
	Sonata in G Minor, (L 386)	M	Twelve Easy Scarlatti Sonatas
SPETH, J. (?)	Fugue in D Minor	K	A Little Book of Fugues (No. 5)
TELEMANN, G. P. (1681-1767)	Fantasia in B-flat	EV	New Recital Repertoire (Mirovitch)
	Fantasia in F, No. II	GS	Introduction to Piano Classics, Vol. III (Mirovitch)
		Sch	Telemann: Kleine Fantasien (No. 5)
	Fantasia in G Minor, No. I	GS	Introduction to Piano Classics, Vol. III (Mirovitch)
		Sch	Telemann: Kleine Fantasien (No. 6)
	Fantasia in G Minor, No. III	GS	Introduction to Piano Classics, Vol. III (Mirovitch)
	Seven Fantasies	Sch	Kleine Fantasien
TURINI, F. (1749-1812)	Molto allegro	HC	Clavecinistes Italiens
		OD	Early Italian Piano Music
	Presto in G Minor	HC	Clavecinistes Italiens

Composer	Title	Publisher	Volume or Collection
ZIPOLI, D. (1675-1726)	Gavotta in B Minor	K	Old Masters of the 16th, 17th and 18th Centuries

	Suite in B Minor
	  Preludio
	  Corrente
	  Aria
	  Gavotta
		OD	Early Italian Piano Music

Composer	Title	Publisher	Volume or Collection
ALBÉNIZ, I. (1860-1909)	Córdoba, Op. 232, No. 4	UME GS	Chants d'Espagne Published Separately
	Granada	UME M	Suite Espagnole No. I Published Separately
	Malagueña	M	Published Separately
	Orientale, Op. 232, No. 2	UME GS	Chants d'Espagne 51 Piano Pieces from the Modern Repertoire
	Seguidillas, Op. 232, No. 5	UME M	Chants d'Espagne Published Separately
	Sevilla	UME M	Suite Espagnole Published Separately
	Tango in D	BMC	Published Separately
	Tango, Op. 164, No. 2	GS	51 Piano Pieces from the Modern Repertoire
	Zambra (From "12 Characteristic Pieces")	S	Les Chefs-D'Oeuvre des Grands Maitres
BEETHOVEN, L. van (1770-1827)	Adagio, (From Sonata Op. 2, No. 1)	K P SS	Beethoven Sonatas, Vol. I
	Adagio cantabile, (From Sonata, Op. 13)	Ox	
	Adagio sostenuto, (From Sonata, Op. 27, No. 2)		
	Allegretto, (From Sonata Op. 27, No. 2)		
	Allegro, (From Sonata Op. 2, No. 1)		
	Allegro molto e con brio, (From Sonata, Op. 10, No. 1)		
	Andante, (From Sonata, Op. 14, No. 2)	K P SS B GS	Beethoven Sonatas, Vol. I Hours with the Masters, Bk. V Master Series for the Young
	Andante, (From Sonata, Op. 79)	K P SS GS	Beethoven Sonatas, Vol. II Master Series for the Young
	Bagatelles, Op. 33 (Complete)	GS P	Bagatelles, Op. 33 Various Pieces

Composer	Title	Publisher	Volume or Collection
BEETHOVEN, L. (cont.)		K	Various Piano Pieces
		GS	Beethoven Easy Compositions
	Bagatelle in B-flat, Op. 119, No. 11	P	Various Pieces
		K	Various Piano Pieces
		GS	Beethoven, Easy Compositions
		K	Easy Compositions by Mozart and Beethoven
		GS	Master Series for the Young
	Bagatelle in C, Op. 119, No. 2	P	Various Pieces
		K	Various Piano Pieces
		H	Easiest Original Pieces
	Bagatelle in C, Op. 119, No. 7	P	Various Pieces
		K	Various Piano Pieces
		GS	Thirty-two Sonatinas and Rondos
	Bagatelle in C, Op. 119, No. 8	P	Various Pieces
		K	Various Piano Pieces
	Bagatelle in C Minor, Op. 119, No. 5	P	Various Pieces
		K	Various Piano Pieces
		GS	Master Series for the Young
	Bagatelle in G, Op. 119, No. 6	P	Various Pieces
		K	Various Piano Pieces
	Bagatelle in G Minor, Op. 119, No. 1	P	Various Pieces
		K	Various Piano Pieces
		K	Easy Compositions by Mozart and Beethoven
		GS	Master Series for the Young
	Menuetto, (From Sonata, Op. 2, No. 1)	K	Beethoven Sonatas, Vol. I
		P	
		SS	
		Ox	
	Menuetto, (From Sonata, Op. 10, No. 3)		
	Menuetto, (From Sonata, Op. 31, No. 3)	K	Beethoven Sonatas, Vol. II
		P	
		SS	
		Ox	
	Rondo in A	K	Various Piano Pieces
		P	Various Pieces
		B	Hours with the Masters, Bk. V
	Rondo in C, Op. 51, No. 1	K	Various Piano Pieces
		P	Various Pieces
		GS	Beethoven Easy Compositions
		GS	Thirty-two Sonatinas and Rondos
		GS	Introduction to Piano Classics, Vol. II (Mirovitch)
	Scherzo, (From Sonata, Op. 2, No. 2)	K	Beethoven Sonatas, Vol. I
		P	
		SS	
		Ox	

Composer	Title	Publisher	Volume or Collection
BEETHOVEN, L. (cont.)	Six Ecossaises	P	Beethoven Ecossaisen und Deutsche Tänze
		K	Easy Compositions by Mozart and Beethoven
		GS	Introduction to Piano Classics, Vol. II (Mirovitch)
	Sonata in D Allegro Menuetto Scherzando	MMC K	The Three Bonn Sonatas Beethoven: Sonatinas
	Sonata in E, Op. 14, No. 1 Allegro Allegretto Rondo	K P SS Ox	Beethoven Sonatas, Vol. I
	Sonata in E-flat Allegro cantabile Andante Rondo	MMC K	The Three Bonn Sonatas Beethoven: Sonatinas
	Sonata in F Minor Larghetto maestoso: Allegro assai Andante Presto		
	Sonata in G Minor, Op. 49, No. 1 Andante Rondo	K P SS Ox GS CF	Beethoven Sonatas, Vol. II Beethoven Easy Compositions Road to Piano Artistry, Vol. IX (Scionti)
	.Variations	K GS	Beethoven Variations, Vol. II
	Eight Variations on "Tandeln und Scherzen"		
	Eight Variations on "Une Fièvre brûlante"		
	Nine Variations on "Quanto è bello"		
	Six Easy Variations on an Original Theme		
	Six Variations on "Nel cor più"		
	Ten Variations on "La Stessa la stessimissa"		
BORODIN, A. (1834-1887)	Nocturne	GS GS	Petite Suite Published Separately
	Serenade	GS GS GS	Petite Suite Published Separately Introduction to Piano Classics, Vol. II (Mirovitch)

Composer	Title	Publisher	Volume or Collection
BRAHMS, J. (1833–1897)	Hungarian Dance in F, No. 7	GS	Hungarian Dances, Vol. I
	Hungarian Dance in F Sharp Minor, No. 5		
	Two Sarabandes	H	Sarabandes and Gigues
	Waltz in B, Op. 39, No. 1	P K GS	Brahms Waltzes, Op. 39
	Waltz in B Minor, Op. 39, No. 11	P K GS B	Brahms Waltzes, Op. 39 Hours with the Masters, Bk. V
	Waltz in C sharp Minor, Op. 39, No. 7	P K GS	Brahms Waltzes, Op. 39
	Waltz in E, Op. 39, No. 2		
	Waltz in E, Op. 39, No. 10		
	Waltz in E, Op. 39, No. 5	H	Contemporaries of Schumann
CERVANTES, I. (1847–1905)	Six Cuban Dances	GS	Six Cuban Dances
CHOPIN, F. (1810–1849)	Marche Funèbre, Op. 72, No. 2	GS	Chopin: Various Compositions
	Mazurka in A Minor, Op. 67, No. 4	K P GS GS	Mazurkas Master Series for the Young
	Mazurka in A Minor, Op. 68, No. 2	P GS K GS	Mazurkas Selected Piano Solos by Romantic Composers, Bk. II
	Mazurka in C, Op. 33, No. 3	P GS K GS B	Mazurkas Chopin Album for the Piano Hours with the Masters, Bk. IV
	Mazurka in C, Op. 68, No. 1	K P GS GS	Mazurkas Selected Piano Solos by Romantic Composers, Bk. III
	Mazurka in G Minor, Op. 67, No. 2	P K GS GS	Mazurkas Master Series for the Young
	Mazurka in G Minor, Op. 24, No. 1	P K GS	Mazurkas

Composer	Title	Publisher	Volume or Collection
CHOPIN, F. (cont.)	Mazurka in F, Op. 63, No. 3	P K GS	Mazurkas
		H	Easiest Original Pieces
	Mazurka in F Minor, Op. 63, No. 2	P K GS	Mazurkas
		H	Easiest Original Pieces
	Nocturne in B-flat Minor, Op. 9, No. 1	P GS K	Nocturnes
	Nocturne in C Sharp Minor	GS	Selected Piano Solos by Romantic Composers, Bk. III
		Su	Recital Repertoire, Bk. III (Podolsky)
	Nocturne in E Minor, Op. 72, No. 1 (Posth.)	P GS K	Nocturnes
	Nocturne in E-flat, Op. 9, No. 2	P GS K	Nocturnes
		GS	Chopin Album for the Piano
	Nocturne in F Minor, Op. 55, No. 1	P GS K	Nocturnes
	Nocturne in G Minor, Op. 15, No. 3	P GS K	Nocturnes
		GS	Chopin Album for the Piano
		H	Easiest Original Pieces
	Nocturne in G Minor, Op. 37, No. 1	P GS K	Nocturnes
		GS	Chopin Album for the Piano
	Polonaise in A, Op. 10, No. 1	P K	Chopin: Twelve Polonaises
		GS	Chopin Polonaises
		GS	Chopin Album for the Piano
	Polonaise in C Minor, Op. 10, No. 2	K	Chopin: Twelve Polonaises
		GS	Chopin Polonaises
		P	
	Polonaise in C Sharp Minor, Op. 26, No. 1	K	Chopin: Twelve Polonaises
		GS	Chopin Polonaises
		P	
		GS	Chopin Album for the Piano
	Prelude in A Minor, Op. 28, No. 2	GS	Chopin Preludes
		K	
		P	Preludes and Rondos
	Prelude in B-flat, Op. 28, No. 21	GS	Chopin Preludes
		K	
		P	Preludes and Rondos

Composer	Title	Publisher	Volume or Collection
CHOPIN, F. (cont.)	Prelude in D-flat, Op. 28, No. 15	GS	Chopin Preludes
		K	
		P	Preludes and Rondos
		GS	Chopin Album for the Piano
		PP	Hundred Best Short Classics, Bk. VI
		GS	Master Series for the Young
		H	Easiest Original Pieces
	Prelude in E, Op. 28, No. 9	GS	Chopin Preludes
		K	
		P	Preludes and Rondos
	Prelude in F Sharp, Op. 28, No. 13	GS	Chopin Preludes
		K	
		P	Preludes and Rondos
	Prelude in G Minor, Op. 28, No. 22	GS	Chopin Preludes
		K	
		P	Preludes and Rondos
	Trois Ecossaises, Op. 72	GS	Chopin: Various Compositions
		GS	Published Separately
	Waltz in A Minor, Op. 34, No. 2	P	Chopin Waltzes
		GS	
		K	
		GS	Chopin Album for the Piano
		GS	Selected Piano Solos by Romantic Composers, Bk. III
		H	Easiest Original Pieces
	Waltz in A-flat, Op. 69, No. 1	P	Chopin Waltzes
		GS	
		K	
	Waltz in B Minor, Op. 69, No. 2	P	Chopin Waltzes
		GS	
		K	
	Waltz in C Sharp Minor, Op. 64, No. 2	P	Chopin Waltzes
		GS	
		K	
		GS	Chopin Album for the Piano
	Waltz in D-flat, Op. 64, No. 1	P	Chopin Waltzes
		GS	
		K	
		GS	Chopin Album for the Piano
	Waltz in E (Posth.) (Aus dem Nachlasse)	P	Chopin Waltzes
		GS	
		K	
		GS	Chopin Album for the Piano
	Walts in E Minor (Posth.) (Aus dem Nachlasse)	P	Chopin Waltzes
		GS	
		K	
	Waltz in F Minor, Op. 72, No. 2	P	Chopin Waltzes
		GS	
		K	
		GS	Master Series for the Young

Composer	Title	Publisher	Volume or Collection
CLEMENTI, M. (1752-1832)	Andante in B-flat	CF	Road to Piano Artistry, Vol. VIII
	Sonata in A, Op. 36, No. 1 Allegro Presto	GS	Clementi Sonatas, Bk. I
	Sonata in B-flat, Op. 47, No. 2 Allegro con brio Andante quasi allegretto Rondo	GS	Clementi Sonatas, Bk. II
	Sonata in D, Op. 26, No. 3 Presto Un poco andante Rondo	GS	Clementi Sonatas, Bk. I
	Sonatina in C, Op. 36, No. 5 Presto Air Suisse Rondo	GS GS GS	Clementi: Six Sonatinas, Op. 36 Album of Sonatinas Thirty-two Sonatinas and Rondos
	Sonatina in D, Op. 36, No. 6 Allegro con spirito Rondo	GS GS CF GS	Clementi: Six Sonatinas, Op. 36 Selected Sonatinas, Bk. II Road to Piano Artistry, Vol. VI (Scionti) Thirty-two Sonatinas and Rondos
	Sonatina in D, Op. 37, No. 2 Allegro assai Menuetto	GS	Clementi: Sonatinas
FERRARI, J. G. (1759-1843)	Sonata in G, No. I Allegro Larghetto Anglaise	Su	Trois Sonates (Podolsky)
	Sonata in C, No. II Spiritoso Andante con espressione Rondo-Allegretto		
	Sonàta in F, No. III Allegro Thema con variazione		
FIELD, J. (1782-1837)	Nocturne in C, No. 17	GS	Field: Eighteen Nocturnes
	Nocturne in C Minor, No. 2	GS	Field: Eighteen Nocturnes
	Nocturne in D Minor, No. 15	GS GS	Field: Eighteen Nocturnes Selected Piano Solos by Romantic Composers, Bk. I
	Nocturne in E Minor, No. 9	GS GS	Field: Eighteen Nocturnes Selected Piano Solos by Romantic Composers, Bk. III
	Nocturne in E-flat, No. 1	GS	Field: Eighteen Nocturnes
	Nocturne in F, No. 18	GS	Field: Eighteen Nocturnes Selected Piano Solos by Romantic Composers, Bk. II

Composer	Title	Publisher	Volume or Collection
GADE, N. (1817–1890)	Fantasy Pieces, Op. 41 　1. In the Forest 　2. Mignon 　3. Fairy Tale 　4. Festive Scene	GS	Fantasy Pieces, Op. 41
GRIEG, E. (1843–1907)	Albumleaf, Op. 28, No. 1	GS P GS	Album-Leaves, Op. 28 Forty-five Selected Compositions for 　Piano, Bk. II
	Albumleaf, Op. 28, No. 4	GS P GS	Album-Leaves, Op. 28 Forty-five Selected Compositions for 　Piano, Bk. II
	Albumleaf, Op. 47, No. 2	P GS GS	Lyrical Pieces, Op. 47 Forty-five Selected Compositions for 　Piano, Bk. I
	Carnival Scene, Op. 19, 　No. 3	P GS	Sketches of Norwegian Life, Op. 19
	Holberg Suite, Op. 40 　1. Prelude 　2. Sarabande 　3. Gavotte 　4. Air 　5. Rigaudon	P GS	Holberg Suite, Op. 40 From Holberg's Time, Op. 40
	March of the Dwarfs, 　Op. 54, No. 3	P GS	Lyrical Pieces, Op. 54
	Mélancolie, Op. 47, No. 5	P GS GS	Lyrical Pieces, Op. 47 Forty-five Selected Compositions for 　Piano, Bk. I
	Norwegian Dance, Op. 54, 　No. 2	P GS	Lyrical Pieces, Op. 54
	On the Mountains, Op. 19, 　No. 1	P GS	Sketches of Norwegian Life
	Scherzo, Op. 54, No. 5	P GS GS	Lyrical Pieces, Op. 54 Forty-five Selected Compositions for 　Piano, Bk. II
	Shepherd's Boy, Op. 54, 　No. 1	P GS	Lyrical Pieces, Op. 54
	Spring Dance, Op. 47, 　No. 6	P GS GS	Lyrical Pieces, Op. 47 Forty-five Selected Compositions for 　Piano, Bk. II
	To Spring, Op. 43, No. 6	P GS GS CF	Lyrical Pieces, Op. 43 Forty-five Selected Compositions for 　Piano, Bk. II Road to Piano Artistry, Vol. VIII (Scionti)

Composer	Title	Publisher	Volume or Collection
GRIEG, E. (cont.)	Traveller's Song, Op. 17, No. 13	P GS	Northern Dances and Folk Tunes, Op. 17 Master Series for the Young
	Valse Impromptu, Op. 47, No. 1	P GS	Lyrical Pieces, Op. 47
HELLER, S. (1813-1888)	A Narrative, Op. 46, No. 30	R GS	Thirty Progressive Studies, Op. 46
	Gipsies III	CF	Road to Piano Artistry, Vol. V (Scionti)
HUMMEL, J. N. (1778-1837)	Rondo in E-flat, Op. 11	GS	Published Separately
KUHLAU, F. (1786-1832)	Rondo in F, Op. 40, No. 3	GS	Thirty-two Sonatinas and Rondos
	Sonatina in A, Op. 59, No. 1 Allegro Rondo	GS	Kuhlau Sonatinas, Bk. I
	Sonatina in A, Op. 60, No. 2 Allegro con spirito Allegro moderato	GS	Kuhlau Sonatinas, Bk. II
	Sonatina in C, Op. 59, No. 3 Allegro con spirito Rondo	GS	Kuhlau Sonatinas, Bk. I
	Sonatina in C, Op. 60, No. 3 Allegro Allegro vivace	GS	Kuhlau Sonatinas, Bk. II
	Sonatina in F, Op. 59, No. 2 Allegro Rondo	GS	Kuhlau Sonatinas, Bk. I
	Sonatina in F, Op. 60, No. 1 Allegro Allegro	GS	Kuhlau Sonatinas, Bk. II
LIADOV, ANATOL (1855-1914)	Fourteen Little Pieces, Op. 2	AMP	The Toy Shop, Op. 2
LISZT, F. (1811-1886)	Au Lac de Wallenstadt	GS GS	Annés de Pèlerinage, Bk. I: Premiere Année "Suisse" Selected Piano Solos by Romantic Composers, Bk. III
	Christmas Tree 1. An Old Christmas Carol 2. The Shepherds at the Manger 3. Chimes 4. In Olden Times 5. Old Provencal Christmas Carol	MP	Liszt: Christmas Tree
	Consolation in E, No. 5	GS PP CF	Consolations; Liebesträume Hundred Best Short Classics, Bk. IV Road to Piano Artistry, Vol. VII (Scionti)

Composer	Title	Publisher	Volume or Collection
LISZT, F. (cont.)	Consolations, Nos. 2, 3, 4, 5, 6	GS	Consolations; Liebesträume
	Liebesträume in A-flat, No. 3	GS GS	Consolations; Liebesträume Published Separately
	Liebesträume in E, No. 2	GS Su	Consolations; Liebesträume Recital Repertoire, Bk. III (Podolsky)
MACDOWELL, E. (1861–1908)	By A Meadow Brook, Op. 51, No. 9	AS	Woodland Sketches, Op. 51
	Four Little Poems, Op. 32 1. The Eagle 2. The Brook 3. Moonshine 4. Winter	AMP GS CF	Four Little Poems
	From "Twelve Etudes" 4. Arabesque 5. In the Forest 6. Dance of the Gnomes 7. Idyll 8. Shadow Dance 9. Intermezzo 10. Melody 11. Scherzino 12. Hungarian	BMC	Twelve Etudes, Op. 59
	In Autumn, Op. 51, No. 4	AS	Woodland Sketches, Op. 51
	March Wind, Op. 46, No. 10	AMP AMP	Twelve Virtuoso Studies, Op. 46 Published Separately
	Polonaise, Op. 46, No. 12	AMP AMP	Twelve Virtuoso Studies, Op. 46 Published Separately
	The Joy of Autumn, Op. 62, No. 10	AS	New England Idylls, Op. 62
	Will O' The Wisp, Op. 51, No. 2	AS	Woodland Sketches, Op. 51
	Witches Dance, Op. 17, No. 2	GS	Published Separately
MENDELSSOHN, F. (1809–1847)	Albumleaf, Op. 117	TP	Songs Without Words
	Andante, Op. 16, No. 3	CF	Road to Piano Artistry, Vol. IX (Scionti)
	Andante cantabile	GS GS	Mendelssohn: Miscellaneous Compositions (Kullak) Master Series for the Young
	Characteristic Piece, Op. 7, No. 6 (With Longing)	GS GS	Mendelssohn: Miscellaneous Compositions (Kullak) Master Series for the Young
	Etude, Op. 104, No. 1	GS CF	Three Etudes from Op. 104 Road to Piano Artistry, Vol. IX (Scionti)
	Fantasy or Caprice, Op. 16, No. 1	GS A	Mendelssohn: Miscellaneous Compositions (Kullak) Beringer's School of Easy Classics: Mendelssohn

Composer	Title	Publisher	Volume or Collection
MENDELSSOHN, F. (cont.)	Prelude in F Minor	Su	Recital Repertoire, Bk. IV (Podolsky)
	Retrospection, Op. 102, No. 2	P GS	Songs Without Words
		GS	Introduction to Piano Classics, Vol. III (Mirovitch)
	Reverie, Op. 85, No. 1	P GS	Songs Without Words
		GS	Selected Piano Solos by Romantic Composers, Bk. III
	Rondo Capriccioso, Op. 14	GS	Mendelssohn: Miscellaneous Compositions (Kullak)
		GS	Published Separately
	Scherzo, Op. 16, No. 2	GS	Mendelssohn: Miscellaneous Compositions (Kullak)
		GS	Published Separately
	Songs Without Words	P GS	Songs Without Words

Op. 19
1. Sweet Remembrance
3. Hunting Song
5. Restlessness

Op. 30
1. Contemplation
2. Unrest
4. The Wanderer
5. The Brook

Op. 38
1. Evening Star
2. Lost Happiness
3. The Poet's Harp
5. Passion
6. Duet

Op. 53
1. On The Seashore
2. Fleecy Clouds
3. Agitation
5. Folk Song
6. The Flight

Op. 62
1. May Breezes
2. The Departure
3. Funeral March
5. Venetian Boat Song III

Op. 67
1. Meditation
2. Lost Illusions
3. Song of the Pilgrim
4. Spinning Song
6. Lullaby

Op. 85
1. Reverie

Composer	Title	Publisher	Volume or Collection
MENDELSSOHN, F. (cont.)	2. The Adieu		
	3. Delirium		
	4. Elegy		
	5. The Return		
	6. Song of the Traveller		
	Op. 102		
	1. Homeless		
	2. Retrospection		
	4. The Sighing Wind		
	5. The Joyous Peasant		
	Sweet Remembrance, Op. 19, No. 1	GS	Introduction to Piano Classics, Bk. III (Mirovitch)
	Two Musical Sketches	A	Beringer's School of Easy Classics: Mendelssohn
	Venetian Boat Song III, Op. 62, No. 5	P GS	Songs Without Words
		GS	Selected Piano Solos by Romantic Composers, Bk. III
SCHUBERT, F. (1797-1828)	Allegretto in C Minor	GS H	Master Series for the Young Easiest Original Pieces
	Andante (From Sonata Op. 120)	K P GS	Sonatas, Vol. I
		GS H	Master Series for the Young Easiest Original Pieces
	Impromptu in A-flat, Op. 90, No. 4	K P GS	Impromptus & Moments Musicaux
		PP	Hundred Best Short Classics, Bk. IV
	Impromptu in A-flat, Op. 142, No. 2	K GS P	Impromptus & Moments Musicaux
	Impromptu in E-flat, Op. 90, No. 2	K P GS	Impromptus and Moments Musicaux
	Menuet (From Sonata Op. 122)	K P GS	Sonatas, Vol. I
		A	Beringer's School of Easy Classics: Schubert
	Moment Musical in A-flat, Op. 94, No. 6	GS P K	Impromptus and Moments Musicaux
		GS	Published Separately
		GS	Selected Piano Solos by Romantic Composers, Bk. III
	Moment Musical in F Minor, Op. 94, No. 3	GS P K	Impromptus and Moments Musicaux
		GS	Published Separately
		GS	Master Series for the Young
		PP	Hundred Best Short Classics, Bk. IV
	Scherzo in A (From Five Piano Pieces)	K	Schubert: Various Piano Compositions

Composer	Title	Publisher	Volume or Collection
SCHUBERT, F. (cont.)	Scherzo in D-flat	GS	Introduction to Piano Classics, Vol. III (Mirovitch)
	Waltzes, Op. 77 (Complete) (12 Valses Nobles) 1. C Major	P GS Su	Schubert Dances Recital Repertoire (Podolsky), Bk. III
	Waltzes, Op. 127 (Complete) (13 last waltzes) 5. F Major	P GS A	Schubert Dances Beringer's School of Easy Classics: Schubert
	Waltz in B, Op. 18a, No. 2	P GS GS	Schubert Dances Introduction to Piano Classics, Vol. III (Mirovitch)
	Waltz in E, Op. 18a, No. 1	P GS GS	Schubert Dances Introduction to Piano Classics, Vol. III (Mirovitch)
	Waltz in E, Op. 18a, No. 11	P GS GS	Schubert Dances Introduction to Piano Classics, Vol. III (Mirovitch)
	Waltz in F sharp minor, Op. 18a, No. 8	P GS GS	Schubert Dances Introduction to Piano Classics, Vol. III (Mirovitch)
	Waltz in G, Op. 18a, No. 3	P GS GS	Schubert Dances Introduction to Piano Classics, Vol. III
	Waltzes (selected) Sets III and V	JF	Schubert Waltzes (Maier)
	Variations on a Theme by Anselm Huttenbrenner	K	Schubert: Various Piano Compositions
SCHUMANN, R. (1810-1856)	A Message, Op. 124, No. 18	K GS	Complete Works, Vol. VI Album Leaves, Op. 124

	Album Leaves, Op. 99
	  1. Ziemlich langsam
	  2. Schnell
	  3. Ziemlich langsam
	  4. Sehr langsam
	  5. Langsam
		GS
		K
			Colored Leaves, Op. 99
			Complete Works, Vol. VI

	Almost Too Serious, Op. 15, No. 10	GS P AMP K	Scenes from Childhood, Op. 15 Complete Works, Vol. III
	Arabesque, Op. 18	K AMP GS P	Complete Works, Vol. III Published Separately

Composer	Title	Publisher	Volume or Collection
SCHUMANN, R. (cont.)	At The Fireside, Op. 15, No. 8	GS P AMP	Scenes from Childhood, Op. 15
		K	Complete Works, Vol. III
	Burla, Op. 124, No. 12	K	Complete Works, Vol. VI
		GS	Album Leaves, Op. 124
	Canon, Op. 124, No. 20	GS	Album Leaves, Op. 124
		K	Complete Works, Vol. VI
	Catch Me, Op. 15, No. 3	GS P AMP	Scenes From Childhood, Op. 15
		B	Hours with the Masters, Bk. V
	Child Falling Asleep, Op. 15, No. 12	GS P AMP	Scenes From Childhood, Op. 15
		CF	Road to Piano Artistry, Vol. IX (Scionti)
	Country Dance, Op. 124, No. 7	GS	Album Leaves, Op. 124
		K	Complete Works, Vol. VI
		H	Easiest Original Pieces
	Entreating Child, Op. 15, No. 4	GS P AMP	Scenes From Childhood, Op. 15
		PP	Hundred Best Short Classics, Bk. V
	Evening Music, Op. 99, No. 6	GS	Colored Leaves, Op. 99
		K	Complete Works, Vol. VI
	Fantastic Dance, Op. 124, No. 5	GS	Album Leaves, Op. 124
		K	Complete Works, Vol. VI
		H	Easiest Original Pieces
	Fantastic Piece, Op. 124, No. 19	GS	Album Leaves, Op. 124
		K	Complete Works, Vol. VI
	Figured Choral, Op. 68, No. 42	P GS	Album for the Young, Op. 68
	Forebodings, Op. 124, No. 2	GS	Album Leaves, Op. 124
		K	Complete Works, Vol. VI
	Frightening, Op. 15, No. 11	GS AMP P	Scenes From Childhood, Op. 15
	Grief's Forebodings, Op. 124, No. 8	GS	Album Leaves, Op. 124
		H	Easiest Original Pieces
		K	Complete Works, Vol. VI
	Grillen, Op. 12, No. 4	GS P AMP	Fantasy Pieces, Op. 12
		K	Complete Works, Vol. II
	Hunting Song, Op. 82, No. 7	GS AMP	Forest Scenes, Op. 82
		K	Complete Works, Vol. V
		GS	Published Separately

Composer	Title	Publisher	Volume or Collection
SCHUMANN, R. (cont.)	Impromptu, Op. 124, No. 1	GS K	Album Leaves, Op. 124 Complete Works, Vol. VI
	Knight of the Hobbyhorse, Op. 15, No. 9	GS AMP P	Scenes From Childhood, Op. 15
	Larghetto, Op. 124, No. 13	GS K	Album Leaves, Op. 124 Complete Works, Vol. VI
	Nachtstücke, Op. 23, No. 4	GS K PP GS	Four Nachtstücke Complete Works, Vol. IV Hundred Best Short Classics, Bk. VI Published Separately
	Novellette, Op. 21	GS P AMP K GS	Eight Novelleten, Op. 21 Complete Works, Vol. IV Published Separately
	Novelette, Op. 99	GS K GS	Colored Leaves, Op. 99 Complete Works, Vol. VI Published Separately (No. 3)
	Perfectly Contented, Op. 15, No. 5	GS AMP P PP	Scenes From Childhood, Op. 15 Hundred Best Short Classics, Bk. V
	Romance in F sharp, Op. 28, No. 2	GS AMP PP	Three Romances Hundred Best Short Classics, Bk. VI
	Romance, Op. 124, No. 11	GS K	Album Leaves, Op. 124 Complete Works, Vol. VI
	Scherzino, Op. 124, No. 3	GS K	Album Leaves, Op. 124 Complete Works, Vol. VI
	Scherzo, Gigue, Romance, and Fughetta, Op. 32	GS K	Scherzo, Gigue, Romance and Fughetta, Op. 32 Complete Works, Vol. IV
	Slumber Song, Op. 124, No. 16	GS K A GS	Album Leaves, Op. 124 Complete Works, Vol. VI Beringer's School of Easy Classics: Schumann Published Separately
	Soaring, Op. 12, No. 2	GS AMP P K	Fantasy Pieces, Op. 12 Complete Works, Vol. II

	Sonata II, Op. 118b
	    Allegro
	    Canon
	    Evening Song
	    Children's Party
		GS
		K
			Three Sonatas for the Young, Op. 118
			Complete Works, Vol. VI

	Sonata III, Op. 118c Allegro	GS K	Three Sonatas for the Young, Op. 118 Complete Works, Vol. VI

Composer	Title	Publisher	Volume or Collection
SCHUMANN, R. (cont.)	Andante Gipsy Dance A Child's Dream		
	The Elf, Op. 124, No. 17	GS K A	Album Leaves, Op. 124 Complete Works, Vol. VI Beringer's School of Easy Classics: Schumann
	The Poet Speaks, Op. 15, No. 13	GS P AMP	Scenes From Childhood, Op. 15
	The Prophet Bird, Op. 82, No. 6	AMP GS K PP GS	Forest Scenes, Op. 82 Complete Works, Vol. V Hundred Best Short Classics, Bk. VII Selected Piano Solos by Romantic Composers, Bk. III

	Three Little Pieces, Op. 99
	  1. Nicht schnell
	  3. Frisch
		GS
		K
			Colored Leaves, Op. 99
			Complete Works, Vol. VI

	Traumerei, Op. 15, No. 7	GS AMP P K PP GS	Scenes From Childhood, Op. 15 Complete Works, Vol. III Hundred Best Short Classics, Bk. IV Published Separately
	Variations on an Original Theme	H	Variations on an Original Theme
	Vision, Op. 124, No. 14	GS K	Album Leaves, Op. 124 Complete Works, Vol. VI
	Waltz, Op. 99, No. 3	GS K	Colored Leaves, Op. 99 Complete Works, Vol. VI
	Waltz, Op. 124, No. 10	GS K	Album Leaves, Op. 124 Complete Works, Vol. VI
	Waltz, Op. 124, No. 15	GS K	Album Leaves, Op. 124 Complete Works, Vol. VI
	Warum, Op. 12, No. 3	GS AMP P K PP	Fantasy Pieces, Op. 12 Complete Works, Vol. II Hundred Best Short Classics, Bk. VII
TSCHAIKOWSKY, P. (1840-1893)	August - Harvest Song, Op. 37a, No. 8	GS	The Seasons, Op. 37a
	December - Christmas, Op. 37a, No. 12	GS GS	The Seasons, Op. 37a Selected Piano Solos by Romantic Composers, Bk. II
	February - Carnival, Op. 37a, No. 2	GS	The Seasons, Op. 37a

Composer	Title	Publisher	Volume or Collection
TSCHAIKOWSKY, P. (cont.)	July - Song of the Reaper, Op. 37a, No. 7	GS	The Seasons, Op. 37a
	June - Barcarolle, Op. 37a, No. 6	GS GS	The Seasons, Op. 37a Selected Piano Solos by Romantic Composers, Bk. III
	March - Song of the Lark, Op. 37a, No. 3	GS	The Seasons, Op. 37a
	Nocturne in C sharp Minor, Op. 19, No. 4	GS	Introduction to Piano Classics, Vol. II (Mirovitch)
	November - Troika, Op. 37a, No. 11	GS GS	The Seasons, Op. 37a Introduction to Piano Classics, Vol. II (Mirovitch)
	September - Hunter's Song, Op. 37a, No. 9	GS	The Seasons, Op. 37a
WEBER, C. (1786-1826)	Mazurka, Op. 10, No. 4	GS	Master Series for the Young
	Rondo, Op. 3, No. 6	GS	Master Series for the Young

Composer	Title	Publisher	Volume or Collection

AURIC, GEORGES (1899-)	Petite Suite
	  1. Prelude
	  2. Danse
	  3. Vilanelle et Entrée
	  4. Sarabande
	  5. Voltes
		HC	Petite Suite

BARTÓK, BÉLA (1881-1945)	An Air	BH	Nine Little Piano Pieces, Bk. II
	Bagatelles, Op. 6 Nos. 2, 5, 8, 9, 11, 13, 14	BH	Fourteen Bagatelles, Op. 6
	From "Four Dirges" Op. 8b, Nos. 2, 3 and 4	BH	Four Dirges, Op. 8b
	Mikrokosmos, Vol. V A Bagpipe	BH	Mikrokosmos, Vol. V
	Mikrokosmos, Vol. VI Ostinato	BH	Mikrokosmos, Vol. VI
	Roumanian Folk Dances Nos. 5 and 6	BH	Roumanian Folk Dances

	Sonatina
	  Bagpipers
	  Bear Dance
	  Finale
		BH	Sonatina

	Three Rondos	BH	Three Rondos on Folk Tunes
	Tambourine	BH	Nine Little Piano Pieces, Bk. II

BATE, STANLEY (1912-)	Six Pieces for an Infant
	  Prodigy
	  1. Very Fast
	  2. Very Simply
	  3. In Quick march time
	  4. Moderately
	  5. Quickly
	  6. Very Fast
		MP	Six Pieces for an Infant Prodigy

	Seven Pieces for Piano
	  1. Prelude
	  2. Romance
	  3. Chanson Populaire
	  4. Moment Musicale
	  5. Polka
	  6. Melodie
	  7. Valse
		Sch	Seven Pieces for Piano

	Sonatina No. 7
	  1. March
	  2. Pastoral
	  3. Tarantella
		AMP	Sonatina, No. 7

138

Composer	Title	Publisher	Volume or Collection
CARPENTER, JOHN ALDEN (1876-)	From "Diversions" 1. Lento 2. Allegretto con moto 4. Moderato	GS	Diversions
COOLS, EUGENE (1879-1936)	From "Our Daughter's Party" 1. The Welcome 6. Let's Dance 7. Leave Taking	E	Our Daughter's Party, Op. 93
COPLAND, AARON (1900-)	The Cat and the Mouse (Scherzo Humoristique)	EV	Published Separately
COWELL, HENRY (1897-)	Celtic Set 1. Reel 2. Caoine 3. Hornpipe	CS	Celtic Set
DEBUSSY, CLAUDE (1862-1918)	Arabesques 1. E Major 2. G Major	EV	Deux Arabesques
	Clair de Lune	EV EV	Suite bergamasque Published Separately
	Danseuses de Delphes	EV EV	Preludes, Bk. I Published Separately
	Golliwog's Cakewalk	EV EV	Children's Corner Published Separately
	Jimbo's Lullaby	EV EV	Children's Corner Published Separately
	La Cathédrale engloutie	EV EV	Preludes, Bk. I Published Separately
	La Fille aux cheveux de lin	EV EV	Preludes, Bk. I Published Separately
	La Plus que lente	EV	Published Separately
	Little Nigar	EV	Published Separately
	Little Shepherd	EV	Published Separately
	Rêverie	EV M GS	Published Separately 51 Piano Pieces from the Modern Repertoire
	Serenade for the Doll	EV EV	Children's Corner Published Separately
	Valse romantique	EV GS	Published Separately 51 Piano Pieces from the Modern Repertoire
DETT, R. NATHANIEL (1882-1943)	Juba Dance	Su	Published Separately

Composer	Title	Publisher	Volume or Collection
DIAMOND, DAVID (1915-)	Sonatina 1. Largo assai 2. Allegretto 3. Allegro vivace	MP	Sonatina
DOHNANYI, ERNST VON (1877-)	From "Bagatelles," Op. 13 1. Dedication 2. March 3. To Ada 7. At Midnight 9. Dawn 10. Postlude	Do M	Winterreigen, Ten Bagatelles, Op. 13 Published Separately
FULEIHAN, ANIS (1900-)	Short Pieces 1. Madrigal 4. Rhythmic Episode 5. Slow Waltz 6. Five-Eight 7. Invention 8. Scherzino 10. Conversation 12. Plaintive Wlatz 14. Reflection	CF	Fifteen Short Pieces
GODOWSKY, LEOPOLD (1870-1938)	Nocturnal Tangier	GS	51 Piano Pieces from the Modern Repertoire
GOOSSENS, EUGENE (1893-)	From "Kaleidoscope," Op. 18 1. Good Morning 2. Promenade 4. March of the Wooden Soldier 5. The Rocking Horse 6. The Punch and Judy Show 7. A Ghost Story 12. Good Night	C	Kaleidoscope, Op. 18
GRANADOS, ENRIQUE (1867-1916)	Spanish Dances 1. Minueto 2. Oriental 3. Zarabanda 4. Villanesca 5. Andaluza (Playera) 6. Jota (Rondalla Aragonese) 7. Valenciana 8. Asturiana 9. Mazurca 10. Danza Triste 11. Zambra 12. Arabesca (Mélancolica)	MMC UME UME UME	Twelve Spanish Dances, Op. 5 Published Separately Published Separately) Published Separately

Composer	Title	Publisher	Volume or Collection

GREEN, RAY (1909-)	Short Sonata in F
	  1. Opening Movement
	  2. Pastorale
	  3. Chorale
	  4. Ending Movement
		AME	Short Sonata in F

GRIFFES, CHARLES (1884-1920)	The Lake at Evening	GS	Published Separately

GROVLEZ, GABRIEL (1879-1944)	From ''A Child's Garden''
	  1. La Sieste
	  2. Choses du Soir
	  3. Chanson de Grand-
	      Père
	  6. Pepita
		C	A Child's Garden

	L'Almanach Aux Images
	  1. Les Marionettes
	  2. Berceuse de la Poupée
	  3. La Sarabande
	  4. Chanson du Chasseur
	  5. Les Anes
	  6. Le Pastour
	  7. Chanson de l'Escarpolette
	  8. Petites Letaines De Jésus
		A	L'Almanach Aux Images

GUION, DAVID (1895-)	The Harmonica Player (From ''Alley Tunes'')	GS	Published Separately
HANSON, HOWARD (1896-)	Clog Dance	CF	Published Separately

IBERT, J. (1895-)	From ''Histoires''
	  2. Le petit âne blanc
	      (The Little White
	      Donkey)
	  4. A Giddy Girl
	  5. Dans la maison triste
	  7. Bajo la mesa
	  8. La cage de cristal
	  9. La Marchande d'eau
	      fraîche
	 10. Le Cortège de Balkis
		Le	Histoires
			Published Separately
			
			Published Separately

IRELAND, JOHN (1879-)	The Island Spell	A	Published Separately
ITURBI, JOSE (1895-)	Pequeña Danza Española	GS	Published Separately

KABALEVSKY, DMITRI (1904-)	Preludes
	  1. C Major
	  2. A Minor
	  3. E Minor
	  8. A Major
	  9. E Major
	 15. D-flat Major
	 20. C Minor
	 23. F Major
		I	24 Preludes, Op. 38

Composer	Title	Publisher	Volume or Collection

KABALEVSKY, DMITRI (cont.)	Sonatina in C, Op. 13, No. 1
	  1. Allegro assai e
	      lusingando
	  2. Andantino
	  3. Presto
		L	Published Separately

KRENEK, ERNEST (1900-)	Little Suite, Op. 13a
	  1. Allemande
	  2. Sarabande
	  3. Gavotte
	  4. Waltz
	  5. Fugue
	  6. Fox Trot
		AMP	Little Suite, Op. 13a

MEDTNER, NIKOLAI (1879-)	Fairy Tale, Op. 14, No. 1	MMC I	Published Separately Album of Selected Pieces: Medtner

MILHAUD, DARIUS (1892-)	Saudades do Brazil, Vol. I
	  1. Sorocabo
	  2. Botafogo
	  3. Leme
	  4. Copacabana
	  5. Ipanema
	  6. Gavea
	
	  Vol. II
	  7. Corcovado
	  8. Tijuca
	  9. Sumaré
	  10. Paineras
	  11. Larendeiras
	  12. Paysandú
		Sch	Saudades do Brazil

MOMPOU, FEDERICO (1893-)	Cançó I Dansa (Song and Dance) Part I	Ax UME	Published Separately

	Scènes d'Enfants
	  1. Cris dans la rue
	  2. Jeux sur la plage
	  3. Jeu
	  4. Jeu
	  5. Jeunes filles au jardin
		EV	Scènes d'Enfants

MOORE, DOUGLAS (1893-)	Suite Dancing School Prelude Processional Reel	CF	Published Separately
PALMGREN, SELIM (1878-)	Cradle Song	BMC	Published Separately

	Five Sketches, Op. 31
	  1. Karelian Dance
	  2. Minuet
	  3. A Guilty Conscience
	  4. Minuet Waltz
	  5. Finlandish Dance
		BMC	Five Sketches from Finland, Op. 31

Composer	Title	Publisher	Volume or Collection
PALMGREN, SELIM (cont.)	May Night	BMC	Published Separately
	Six Lyric Pieces, Op. 28 　1. Preludium 　2. The Isle of Shadows 　3. Legend 　4. A Mother's Song 　5. The Swan 　6. Roundelay	BMC	Six Lyric Pieces, Op. 28
PERSICHETTI, VINCENT (1915-　)	Variations for an Album	MP	Published Sparately
PINTO, OCTAVIO (1890-1950)	From "Memories of Childhood" 　1. Run, Run 　2. Ring Around the Rosy 　5. Hobby Horse	GS	Memories of Childhood
	Tom Thumb's March	GS GS	Published Separately 51 Pieces from the Modern Repertoire
POULENC, FRANCIS (1889-　)	Mouvements perpétuels	C	Mouvements perpétuels
PROKOFIEFF, SERGE (1891-1953)	Gavotte, Op. 12, No. 2	GS Ax	Published Separately Serge Prokofieff Album
	March, Op. 12, No. 1	GS Ax	Published Separately Serge Prokofieff Album
	Prelude, Op. 12, No. 7	GS Ax	Published Separately Serge Prokofieff Album
	Tales of the Old Grand- mother, Op. 31 　1. Moderato 　2. Andantino 　3. Andante assai 　4. Sostenuto	L AMP	Tales of the Old Grandmother, Op. 31
REBIKOV, VLADIMIR (1866-1920)	Les Démons s'amusent	GS MMC	51 Piano Pieces from the Modern Repertoire Published Separately
RESPIGHI, OTTORINO (1879-1936)	Notturno	GS GS	Published Separately 51 Piano Pieces from the Modern Repertoire
REUTTER, HERMANN (1900-　)	Variations on a Children's Song, Op. 28	Sch	The New Piano Book, Vol. II
ROZSA, MIKLOS (1907-　)	From "Kaleidoscope," Op. 19 Burlesque Zingara	AMP	Published Separately
SCHMITT, FLORENT (1870-　)	Pacing	CF	Masters of Our Day

Composer	Title	Publisher	Volume or Collection
SCOTT, CYRIL (1879-)	Danse Négre, Op. 58, No. 5	G	Published Separately
	Guttersnipes' Dance	Sch	The New Piano Book, Vol. III
	Lento from "Two Pierrot Pieces"	BH	Published Separately
	Lotus Land, Op. 47, No. 1	G	Published Separately
SCRIABINE, ALEXANDER (1872-1915)	Preludes, Op. 11 2. A Minor 4. E Minor 9. E Major 10. C Sharp Minor 13. G-flat Major 15. D-flat Major 17. A-flat Major 22. G Minor	MMC Ax	Preludes, Op. 11
SÉVÉRAC, D. de (1873-1921)	From "En Vacances" Series I 6. An Old Music Box 7. Romantic Waltz	S	En Vacances - Series I
SHOSTAKOVITCH, DMITRI (1906-)	Polka, Op. 22	L GS I	Published Separately 51 Piano Pieces from the Modern Repertoire Album of Selected Piano Works (Shostakovitch)
	Preludes, Op. 34 Nos. 2, 7, 13, 14, 15, 16, 17, 19, 22, 24	L I	Twenty Four Preludes, Op. 34
	Selected Preludes from Op. 34, Nos. 13, 16, 17, 24	Ax	Selected Preludes
	Three Fantastic Dances, Op. 1	L Ax I	Three Fantastic Dances, Op. 1 Album of Selected Piano Works (Shostakovitch)
SIBELIUS, JEAN (1865-)	Air Castles (Prelude) Op. 46, No. 1	BMC	From The Land of a Thousand Lakes
	Alla Gavotta, Op. 46, No. 7		
	Love Sorrow, Op. 57, No. 2		
	Nocturne, Op. 51, No. 3		
	Romance, Op. 24, No. 9	GS	51 Piano Pieces from the Modern Repertoire
	Sunset, Op. 46, No. 8	BMC	From the Land of a Thousand Lakes
	Valse Mélancolique, Op. 54, No. 3		
SLAVENSKI, JOSIP (1865-1930)	Slowenisches Volkslied	Sch	The New Piano Book, Vol. III

Composer	Title	Publisher	Volume or Collection
STRAUSS, RICHARD (1864-1951)	Traumerei (Reverie), Op. 9, No. 4	GS GS	Published Separately 51 Piano Pieces from the Modern Repertoire
STRAVINSKY, IGOR (1882-)	Valse	Sch	The New Piano Book, Vol. III
SWANSON, HOWARD (1909-)	The Cuckoo (Scherzino)	L	Published Separately
TANSMAN, ALEXANDRE (1897-)	Four Impressions 1. Prelude 2. Invention 3. Nocturne 4. Burlesque	L	Four Impressions
	Four Piano Moods	L	Four Piano Moods
	From "Petite Suite" 3. Meditation 5. Plainte orientale 7. Scherzino	E	Petite Suite
TCHÉREPNINE, ALEXANDRE (1899-)	Bagatelles, Op. 5 1. Allegro marciale 2. Con vivacita 3. Vivo 4. Lento con tristezza 5. Dolce 6. Allegro con spirito 7. Prestissimo 8. Allegro 9. Allegretto 10. Presto	I HC	Bagatelles, Op. 5
	Expressions, Op. 81 1. Entrance 3. Caprice 4. The Silly Story of the White Oxen 5. The Fleeting Vision 6. At the Fair 7. Barcarolle 8. Blind Man's Buff 9. At Dawn 10. Exit	L	Expressions, Op. 81
	From "Pour petits et grands", Set I 1. La Diligente Set II 3. La Persévérante 5. Les Plaisirs du Toutou 6. La Belle au Bois Dormant	D	Pour petits et grands
	Intermezzo	Sch	The New Piano Book, Vol. II
	Petite Suite 1. Marche	D	Petite Suite

Composer	Title	Publisher	Volume or Collection
TCHÉREPNINE, ALEXANDRE (cont.)	2. Chant sans paroles 3. Berceuse 4. Scherzo 5. Badinage 6. Humoresque		
	Piéces sans titres (Pieces without Names) 1. Allegro 2. Allegretto 3. Moderato 4. Andantino 5. Allegro molto 6. Sostenuto 7. Allegretto 8. Impetuoso	D	Piéces sans titres
THOMSON, VIRGIL (1896-)	Piano Sonata, No. 4 1. Allegro 2. Adagio 3. Vivace	EV	Published Separately
TOCH, ERNST (1887-)	Dance for Ruth (From ''Tanz und Spielstücken'' Op. 40)	Sch	The New Piano Book, Vol. II

TURINA, JOAQUIN (1882-)	At the Shoemakers
	 1. Hans Sachs
	 2. The Marquise's
	     Silken Slippers
	 3. The Peasant's Boots
	 4. Greek Sandals
	 5. The Shoes of the
	     Ballet Dancer
	 6. The Dainty Shoes of
	     Her Ladyship
	 7. Shoes of a Toreador
		Sch	At the Shoemakers

	Miniatures 1. Out for a Walk 2. Soldiers Are Coming 3. The Village is Asleep 4. Dawn 5. The Market Place 6. Duo sentimental 7. The Festival 8. The Return	AMP	Miniatures
	The Circus 1. Fanfare 2. Jugglers 3. Equestrienne 4. The Trained Dog 5. Clowns 6. Trapeze Artists	AMP	The Circus
VILLA-LOBOS, HEITOR (1887-)	Alnilam (No. 2 from ''The Three Maries'')	CF	Masters of Our Day

Composer	Title	Publisher	Volume or Collection
VILLA-LOBOS, HEITOR (cont.)	Alnitah (No. 1 from "The Three Maries")		
	Five Pieces, Album VII 1. In My Backyard 2. Go, Pumpkin 3. Let's Go, Maruca 4. The Little Doves 5. Round the Circle	MP	Five Pieces on Children's Folk Tunes of Brazil, Album 7
	From "Guia Prático" Album IX 1. The Little Orange Tree 2. Little Dove, Tiny Dove 4. The Old Woman That Had Nine Daughters 6. The Castle	VL	Guia Prático Album 9
	Pierrette's Hands	Ax	Published Separately

KEY TO PUBLISHERS

A	Augener & Co., London (Broude Bros., 56 W. 45th St. N. Y. C.)
AME	American Music Edition, 250 W. 57th St., N. Y. 19
AMP	Associated Music Publishers, 25 W. 45th St., N. Y. C.
AS	Arthur P. Schmidt Co., Inc., 120 Boylston St., Boston, Mass.
Ax	Axelrod Publications, Inc., 45 Snow St., Boston, Mass.
B	Belwin, Inc., Rockville Centre, L. I., N. Y.
BH	Boosey and Hawkes, 30 W. 57th St., Boston, Mass.
BMC	Boston Music Co., 116 Boylston St., Boston, Mass.
C	Chester Ltd., London (Edward Marks)
CF	Carl Fischer, Inc., Cooper Square, N. Y. C.
D	Durand et fils Paris (Elkan-Vogel Co.)
De	Delkas Music Publishing Co., (Leeds)
Do	Ludwig, Doblinger, Vienna (Associated Music Publishers)
E	Max Eschig, Paris (Associated Music Publishers)
EV	Elkan-Vogel Co., 1716 Sansom St., Philadelphia 3, Penna.
G	Galaxy Music Corporation, 47 W. 46th St., N. Y. C.
GS	G. Schirmer, Inc., 3 E. 43rd St., N. Y. C.
H	Hinrichsen Edition (Peters)
HC	Heugel & Cie, London (Mercury Music Corp.)
He	Heritage Music Publications, Inc., W. 63rd St., N. Y. 23
Ho	Chas. Homeyer & Co., 458 Boylston St., Boston, Mass.
I	International Music Co., 509 Fifth Ave., N. Y. C.
JF	J. Fischer & Bro., 119 W. 40th St., N. Y. C.
K	Edwin F. Kalmus, 112 W. 89th St., N. Y. C.
L	Leeds Music Corp., RKO Bldg., Radio City, N. Y. C.
Le	A. Leduc, Paris (M. Baron Co., 8 W. 45th St., N. Y., 36)
M	Edward Marks Music Corp., RCA Bldg., N. Y. C.
MM	Mills Music, Inc., 1619 Broadway, N. Y. 19
MMC	Mercury Music Corp., 47 W. 63rd St., N. Y., 23
MP	Music Press (Now Mercury Music Corp.)
O	Omega Music Edition, 19 W. 44th St., N. Y. C.
OD	Oliver Ditson, 179 Tremont St., Boston, Mass.
Ox	Oxford University Press, London (114 Fifth Ave., N. Y. C.)
P	C. F. Peters, Leipsig, 881 Seventh Ave., N. Y. C.
PP	Paterson's Publications Ltd, London, (Carl Fischer, Inc.)
R	G. Ricordi & Co., Milan (132 W. 21st St., N. Y. C.)
S	Salabert, Inc., 1 E. 57th St., N. Y. C.
Sch	Schott & Co., London, Brussels, (Associated Music Publishers)
SG	Schroeder & Gunther, 6 E. 45th St., N. Y. C.
So	Sothern Music Publishing Co., 1619 Broadway, N. Y. C.
SS	Simon and Schuster, 386 Fourth Ave., N. Y. C.
Su	Clayton Summy Co., 235 So. Wabash Ave., Chicago, Ill.
TP	Theodore Presser Co., Bryn Mawr, Penna.
U	Universal Music Co., (Associated Music Publishers. Also 59 E. Van Buren St., Chicago 5, Ill.)
UME	Union Musical Española (Associated Music Publishers)
W	Willis Music Co., 137 W. Fourth St., Cincinnati, Ohio
Wo	B. F. Wood, Inc., 24 Brooklyn Ave., Boston, Mass.
VL	Villa-Lobos Music Corp., 1585 Broadway, N. Y. 19

INDEX OF COMPOSERS